Other Books by Frances Wood

Our National Parks Series

YELLOWSTONE, GLACIER, GRAND TETON
GRAND CANYON, ZION, BRYCE CANYON
YOSEMITE, SEQUOIA AND KINGS CANYON, HAWAII
ROCKY MOUNTAIN, MESA VERDE, CARLSBAD CAVERNS
GREAT SMOKY MOUNTAINS, EVERGLADES, MAMMOTH CAVE
MOUNT RAINIER, MOUNT MCKINLEY, OLYMPIC

Enchantment of America Series

PANORAMIC PLAINS
GULF LANDS AND CENTRAL SOUTH
LAKES, HILLS AND PRAIRIES
MEXICO

Other Books by Dorothy Wood

BEAVERS
PLANTS WITH SEEDS
LONG EYE AND THE IRON HORSE

Enchantment of America Series

SEA AND SUNSHINE
HILLS AND HARBORS
NEW ENGLAND COUNTRY
CANADA

Science Parade Series

THE BEAR FAMILY
THE CAT FAMILY

ANIMALS IN DANGER
The Story of Vanishing American Wildlife

FRANCES and DOROTHY WOOD

Illustrated with photographs

DODD, MEAD & COMPANY · NEW YORK

Picture Credits

The illustrations in this book are used through the courtesy of the following (photographers' names included where available):

Bureau of Sport Fisheries and Wildlife, Fish and Wildlife Service, U.S. Department of the Interior: pages 15, 149; Winston Banko, 96, 155; Luther C. Goldman, 30, 36–37, 37, 43, 47 (left), 129, 135, 137, 141, 160; Great Bend City Park, Great Bend, Kansas, 95; E. P. Haddon, 16, 65, 92; Robert D. Jones, Jr., 106–7; E. R. Kalmbach, 133; George B. Kelez, 146; Carl B. Koford, 53; Willis Peterson, 138; Don Pfitzer, 61; V. B. Scheffer, 115; Rex Gary Schmidt, 47 (right); Richard Thompson, 62; Willard A. Troyer, 110; Peter J. Van Huizen, 166.

California Department of Fish and Game: 8 (photograph by New Mexico Department of Fish and Game); W. G. Macgregor, 70–71.

Dr. Archie Carr: 103.

Ed Cesar, from National Audubon Society: 12.

Colorado Game, Fish and Parks Department: Don Domenick, x, 25, 144.

Florida Game and Fresh Water Fish Commission: 4, 81; E. M. DeFoor, 3; Bill Hansen, 84; Gene Smith, 78.

Florida State News Bureau: 76, 102, 118–19.

Robert C. Hermes, from National Audubon Society: 99.

Michigan Department of Conservation: ii, 23, 50, 153.

Wilford L. Miller, from National Audubon Society: 5.

Montana Fish and Game Department: I & E Division photo, 157.

National Audubon Society: 33 (Reprinted from the May/June issue of *Audubon*, copyright © 1960, National Audubon Society. Used by permission.); 122 (The painting by Guy Coheleach is reprinted from the November/December issue of *Audubon*, copyright © 1967, National Audubon Society. Used by permission.)

National Park Service, U.S. Department of the Interior: Everglades National Park, 126–27; Robert T. Haugen, vi; Grand Canyon National Park, 74.

North Carolina Wildlife Resources Commission: Jack Dermid, 85, 90.

W. J. Schoonmaker, from National Audubon Society: 19.

U.S. Coast Guard: 67.

Acknowledgments

For invaluable help in assembling information and for critically reading portions of the manuscript, the authors are grateful to: Personnel of the U.S. Bureau of Sport Fisheries and Wildlife: Dr. Ray C. Erickson, Assistant Director, Patuxent Wildlife Research Center; Harry A. Goodwin, Chief, Office of Endangered Species; Donald J. Hankla, Wildlife Management Biologist; Phillip S. Morgan, Manager, Charles L. Ward, and Earl L. Benham, Aransas Wildlife Refuge; Max W. Walker, Manager, Key Deer Refuge; and Beatrice Boone, Photo Librarian, Office of Conservation Education.

Dr. Archie Carr, Graduate Research Professor, Department of Zoology, University of Florida; Louis S. Clapper, Chief, Division of Conservation Education, National Wildlife Federation; Helen Gere Cruickshank, naturalist and author; D. W. Douglass, Chief, Game Division, Michigan Department of Conservation; Mrs. Beula Edmiston, Secretary, Committee for the Preservation of the Tule Elk; George W. Irvine, Wildlife Biologist, Huron-Manistee National Forests; John Kieran, naturalist and author; Thomas L. Kimball, Executive Director, National Wildlife Federation.

National Audubon Society: Charles M. Brookfield, Southeast Field Representative; Les Line, Editor, *Audubon* magazine; Shirley Miller, Director, Audubon Junior Program; Alexander Sprunt, IV, Research Director.

William M. Partington, Assistant Director, Florida Audubon Society; Dr. William B. Robertson, Jr., Research Biologist, Everglades National Park; Dr. Peter L. Sguros, Department of Biological Sciences, Florida Atlantic University; Walter T. Shannon, Director, California Department of Fish and Game; Howard B. Stricklin, Superintendent, and Merrill D. Beal, Chief Naturalist, Grand Canyon National Park.

We are indebted to the National Audubon Society and to Charles H. Callison, Executive Vice President, for permission to use the quotation on page 38, from *The Whooping Crane*: Research Report No. 3, by Robert Porter Allen; and to the National Audubon Society and Les Line, Editor, for permission to use the two quotations on page 168, from the *Audubon* magazine.

*Myriads of animals feed in the mud and shallow water of wetlands.
Here wood ibis and roseate spoonbills dredge grubs and other food
from the mucky bottom.*

Introduction

NO ROOM FOR ANIMALS?

Is it a forest? Clear it!

Is it a prairie? Plow it!

Is it a swamp? Drain it!

Is it an island? Build a causeway to it!

Is it a shore? Dredge up the bottom of the sea and build land out from it!

Wanting land and more land is one of the great forces in the lives of today's people. With steadily increasing insistence, they want land for homes, land for farms, land for factories.

As they take over the land and develop it, what becomes of the birds and other animals that once lived there? A wetland area for example, supports a great multitude of animals and plants—worms, crabs, oysters, clams, shrimps, snails, insects of many kinds, muskrats, otters, beavers; algae, duckweed, arrowhead, grasses, cattails—and on and on, through a long, long list. These wetland plants and animals are an important part of the living world; they are a vital food supply for many kinds of fish from the open water and for many animals from the land—herons and whooping cranes, alligators and raccoons, eagles and kites, and many more.

When the water is drained and the land dried out, what happens to the animals? Someone said, "Oh, they go somewhere else." But often they don't—because often there is no "somewhere else."

A swamp is drained—and its wildlife dies. A forest is cleared—and its wildlife is forever gone. If only that tree at the end of your street is cut, a wildlife habitat is destroyed and animals are left without a home.

This process is going on all the time around us. It is the biggest single reason for danger to our animals. It has driven some of them into extinction and may take others.

This book tells the story of some of these animals—of some that are in danger today and others that have been endangered and may be again, because man has taken over or destroyed their natural habitat. It reports, too, on other practices of man that have added to danger to our wildlife.

For even though he is taking over much of their habitat, man has not been content to let animals survive in the homes he has left them. He may set out to destroy some kind of animal because he thinks it is a threat to his livestock; he feels there is not enough room for both. Or his chemicals may poison the air or water. Or, for gain or the pleasure of hunting, he may kill too many of one kind of animal. Man is, with some justice, called "the greatest predator." He is the only species that has completely wiped out some other species.

But the book tells also the happier story of some of the work being done to save endangered wildlife. We can say with assurance that today man is becoming more and more aware of a most important fact: If the last whooping crane dies, or the last condor, or the last ivory-billed woodpecker, or the last grizzly bear, that kind of animal is gone forever. We cannot make another one.

So for some of our animals, help may have come in time to save room for them.

CONTENTS

Chapter 1

THE MOUNTAIN LION

"Killer!"

"Predator!"

"Sheep-killer!"

"Kill him! He's worth fifty dollars dead!"

"Kill him before he kills you!"

White men have spoken in these terms about the mountain lion ever since they came to the American continents and found him here. That no good could come of him has been believed and acted upon by most Americans until only recently.

Once this big cat boasted the most far-flung homelands of any mammal in the western hemisphere. From British Columbia in Canada, he ranged over most of North, Central, and South America. Today, south of the United States, he is still fairly common. But in the United States and Canada he lives almost entirely in remote wilderness—in mountains, deserts, and swampy grasslands, as far from people as he can go.

Even in these places, he is disappearing, or, at best, is barely holding his own.

Watch a cat—any cat—go about his daily life of hunting and defending himself. You will see a long, slim body moving stealthily on padded feet that let a cat stalk his prey without making a sound. From these padded feet he can flash strong, sharp claws, one on each toe. He can leap quickly and far, on lithe, strongly

The mountain lion is also called cougar, puma, and panther.

muscled legs. He can fasten strong jaws and sharp teeth on the neck or back of an animal he is catching.

Cats see well at night, because their eyes are especially sensitive to light. The pupils close to slits, letting in only a little light, and so protect the eyes from bright daylight. But in the dark the pupils open big and round, and all the night's light reaches into the cat's eyes. So he sees well at night, and he can stalk his prey unseen, and keep a sharp lookout for danger to himself.

He has sharp ears. He can smell any animal that comes near him. He usually knows more about what is going on around him than any other animal in the wild.

The mountain lion has all these advantages and still another—his size. He measures seven to eight feet long, including his long, round tail, and he weighs from 100 to 150 pounds. But he eats fresh meat only, and it takes a lot of hunting to keep that much lion from going hungry. So getting food for himself, day after day, winter and summer, is a major problem and his chief occupation.

Deer are the favorite food of a mountain lion, and he brings one down much as a house cat goes after a bird or a mouse. He hunts at dusk, or at dawn, or in the dark hours between, when the deer are eating too. Silently he creeps up on a herd of deer, his tan color blending with the ground or rocks or open woods around him. Slowly, slowly he comes closer and closer to one of the feeding deer.

Then he gathers his powerful legs under him—and springs. If he is successful, he lands on the deer's shoulder or back, throwing it forward to the ground. If he misses and the deer leaps away, he does not try to overtake it; it can run faster than he can. He must succeed the first time, or he has lost.

When he kills a deer, he eats what he wants. Then he may drag the rest of it to a place where he can bury it under leaves and twigs. For several days he will return to it to eat. But he will not eat the meat after it begins to spoil. He leaves it then and looks for another deer.

The mountain lion travels through a "range," covering perhaps twenty-five miles in a single night. When the hunting is good, he stays in his range—perhaps an area of rocky hills, with river bottom and brushy flats or open woods, or an area of canyons, or of mountains, or of swampy country. If the hunting is not good, he moves along to a place where it is better.

He eats other animals besides deer—mountain sheep and goats, if he can catch them, woodchucks, wild pigs, rabbits—any small mammals that come his way. He sometimes helps himself to man's animals, too, especially calves, lambs, and colts. But above all, he seems to prefer deer. He most often lives where deer are plentiful.

The big cat launches his spring at a deer he has been stalking.

Eyes, ears, nose—all help a mountain lion in the wild.

So, even though his need for food looms large, he seems quite capable of getting it. And he also seems able to take care of himself in the process. He is so secretive, so night-loving and night-living, that few people have seen him in the wild. And almost no other wild animal is his serious enemy, unless you count the porcupine, whose quills can stick in a mountain lion's nose as easily as in any other animal's.

Still, for all his advantages, no mountain lion lives forever. Is there another lion to replace him when he dies?

Mountain lions mate at any time of year, but most often in late fall, in winter, or very early in the spring, and the kittens are born in spring or summer. The male lion usually leaves the female long before the kittens arrive, and she cares for them by herself—two or three, usually, but sometimes five or six. Their home is in a cave or a deep thicket of bushes and trees.

The kittens are blind and helpless at first, and their mother feeds them with her milk, as all mammals do. Later she brings them meat, and still later she takes them with her and teaches them to hunt for themselves. But for a year or longer, they are more or less defenseless, and dependent on their mother. They tease her and frolic with each other, growling and spitting fiercely. But if any real danger threatens them, such as the attack

of an eagle, their mother takes over and fights off the marauder.
She is a good mother, keeping them safe and well fed.

The kittens are about two years old before they leave her,
and often another year goes by before she has a new litter. Moreover, she herself is about three years old before she has any kittens at all.

Compare the number of her babies with those of a mother
deer, who may have her first fawn before she is a year old, and
probably two fawns a year from then on. Clearly, many more
fawns are born each year than mountain lion kittens. More than
that, the kittens are dependent upon their mother for a much
longer time. They look to her for food long after the fawns are

*These very young kittens have opened their eyes and are beginning to
play in the sunshine outside their den. Their spots will gradually fade,
but will show until they are nearly full grown.*

eating the same leaves and plants that their mother eats. And the kittens have to learn the skill of stalking prey that may be faster and wiser than they are, while all the fawn needs to do is put down its head and eat.

Still, lion kittens are sturdy little creatures. Under ordinary conditions, they are strong and full of life, and enough of them grow up each year to more than make up for the older ones that die of natural causes.

Here, then, is an animal capable of producing effective numbers of his own kind, and talented as few other animals are, for living in whatever wilds he finds himself. So why should there be any question of the mountain lion "holding his own"? Why has he vanished from most of North America, where once he lived far and wide in almost every kind of outdoors we have?

The answer is not in anything that he is or does; it is in what man does. Man is the mountain lion's one terrible enemy, with methods for hunting him that he cannot stand against.

Since white men first came to North America, they have hunted the mountain lion with a remorseless intent to exterminate him. The Indians respected him, some of them enough to make him a religious symbol. Apparently they, too, seldom saw him, for he is rare in their pictures on rock walls and rawhide.

But early in the colonies' history, white men paid bounties for mountain lions—a fixed price and a high one for each dead lion. The lions were trapped, poisoned, and hunted down by packs of dogs. Lion-hunting has always been considered one of the most thrilling of sports. It requires a pack of trained dogs to find and "tree" the lion. The dogs pick up the scent of the lion's tracks and follow him until they catch up with him. He runs for the nearest tree, the dogs keep him in it, and men, following the dogs on horseback, shoot him. None of his fine talent for living in the wild is any good to him here!

So the mountain lion became more and more wary of man,

and moved back and back, deeper into the wilderness. If he ventured into his old haunts, where man was establishing farms and building towns, he was quickly killed. Professional hunters, who received a bounty of fifty dollars or more for each lion killed, could well afford to give all their time to hunting. They assembled big packs of hunting dogs and trained them well. And they were heroes wherever they went—they were ridding the country of a "dangerous menace."

The great naturalist Audubon wrote a description of a lion hunt in which he took part. Men and a dog pack trailed a wounded lion for hours through a swamp in Mississippi. Finally the exhausted lion went into a tree to rest, and was soon shot down from it. The naturalist went on to describe the evening in camp—"the beauties of that nature from which I have certainly derived my greatest pleasures." Apparently, even to Audubon, the mountain lion had no place in the "beauties of nature."

About one hundred years later, a rancher in Colorado who had a pack of "lion dogs" trailed and killed a mother lion. Knowing that she had young kittens somewhere in a den, he said, "I'll find 'em. They're worth fifty dollars apiece to me." And find them he did, after he and his dogs had hunted the rimrocks for a week. There were three of them, and they brought him three more bounty payments.

Few animals, if any, can stand against man, and his guns, and his dogs.

All through the hundred years between these two stories, men hunted the mountain lion. He killed deer, and he killed ranchers' stock, and he was a menace to people, they said. And so they wiped him out in the East, and before long there were almost no lions east of the Rocky Mountains. In all this time, people really learned very little about the mountain lion, except how to kill him.

The price on the mountain lion's head has been canceled nearly everywhere.

Then something happened that made people take a more careful look at him, and at other "predators" as well. On the north rim of the Grand Canyon in Arizona, Grand Canyon National Park and Kaibab National Forest spread northward for many miles on the Kaibab Plateau. Here was the home of a superb herd of mule deer—sleek, well fed, strong, and proud. Government officials in charge of them wanted to keep them that way forever—wanted to protect them from hunting and from predators.

So hunting was outlawed, and a campaign was launched against predators. Some coyotes and eagles were killed. Wolves —there were only a few—were wiped out. But the big blow was against the mountain lions. Nearly eight hundred were killed.

Then, of course, as the planners had expected, the protected deer began to increase. But they increased very much faster than the planners had expected. The herd of about four thousand jumped to twenty thousand, to fifty thousand, and in the next few years, one hundred thousand.

Deer, like lions, have to eat, and they eat plants—"browse plants" with succulent leaves, and the twigs and leaves of small bushes. Grass they eat if they have to—but they take the browse plants first.

The big herd on the Kaibab took everything—all the browse plants, all the leaves of trees as high as they could reach, all the grass. Plants were eaten so deeply into the roots that they died. The Kaibab, once lush with many kinds of vegetation, was eaten to the bone, its soil left bare. Not for many years to come would it again support a herd of deer.

The deer could not leave to find food elsewhere, because the Kaibab is a high plateau surrounded by deep canyons and by desert. So they starved to death—thousands of them. Other thousands, weakened, died of disease. Those that survived were weak and sick. The beautiful, proud Kaibab herd had been destroyed by man's efforts to "protect" it.

Moreover, there was no longer range for the thousands of sheep and cattle that stockmen had once pastured on the Kaibab. So the stockmen had lost far more than the occasional sheep or calf that the lions took.

Similar things were happening in other parts of the country. And gradually people were learning an important fact—that every animal has its own natural place in the wild, and what it is and what it does affect the other living things around it. Its influence on the life around it may not always show up at first glance—but it may be, nevertheless, very important and very far reaching.

Man, therefore, is today taking another look at the mountain lion. He is trying to understand that mountain lions and deer lived together on the Kaibab for hundreds—for thousands—of years before he came along; that the deer survived their natural enemies and developed into a splendid herd without "protection." He begins to realize that, although a lion may kill thirty or forty deer a year, it is the old, the weak, the sick that are most likely to go down under attack. So the lion helps keep the deer herd healthy and strong.

People are also learning that many of the stories of a lion attacking a human being are not true—that the lion runs from humans if he is not cornered. He has a great curiosity, just as a house cat has, and he has startled more than one hiker by trailing him for miles. But a lion attacking a person, unprovoked, is a very rare thing indeed.

So, if he is a good neighbor, if he has a useful place in the living world, should he be wiped out? In recent years, one after another of the states in this country have taken a thoughtful look at their bounty laws. In many places there have been hot arguments. The bounty hunters wanted to keep their hunting grounds and be paid for the lions they killed. The deer hunters wanted their deer unmolested by lions. The stockmen wanted to be sure their stock was safe.

But, gradually, many people took a stand against exterminating the mountain lion. A Colorado rancher, for example, told a reporter, "I've never lost any stock to the mountain lions—and I know they're up yonder," nodding to where his ranchlands climbed into the mountains, "because I find where they've killed a deer every now and then."

And a Colorado boy wrote to one of the state magazines: "I think Colorado should abolish the bounty. I like to go with my Dad to hunt a lion for sport, and I want some lions to be here when my sons go hunting."

So, one by one, the states have ruled against the bounty; only one, Arizona, still pays it. Lions are still hunted in nearly all the states, but they are hunted for sport, not for pay. The hunters must buy licenses, and each hunter is limited to one or two or three lions in a season. Sometimes the season in which lions can be hunted is only two or three months long.

Two states have passed laws against hunting mountain lions at any time. One of these is South Dakota, where only a few lions have survived. The other is Florida, where there are from two hundred to three hundred living in the Everglades—mostly in Everglades National Park.

Florida is the only state where it is believed that mountain lions are increasing. Everywhere else in North America—in Canada and Mexico as well as in the United States—they are barely holding their own, or are decreasing. There are probably not more than six to seven thousand mountain lions in the whole United States, and these are mostly in the western mountain and desert states—no more than a few hundred in each state.

In the years to come, will the few hundred go too? More and more land is being used for farms and towns, where once there were open country and wilderness. So there is less and less true wilderness where mountain lions are most at home—where they survive most successfully. And, as we have seen, not many lion kittens are born each year, and they are subject to danger for many months. If their mother is killed by a hunter, the whole litter is wiped out. If food is scarce, the kittens may be weak and die from disease. Gradually, the few hundred could die out.

Still, the mountain lion may have a chance. Without a price on his head, not nearly so many hunters will be after him. Deer, his natural food, are increasing, and so his own hunting becomes easier.

So perhaps America's big cat will survive. If you're very lucky, you may catch a glimpse of him some night along a lonely road in the West or in Florida, his long body tawny in the headlights of your car and his eyes two yellow-gold reflectors. Or you may hear his unearthly caterwauling, as he calls his mate.

Chapter 2

THESE, TOO, ARE PREDATORS

Great fleas have little fleas upon their backs to bite 'em,
And little fleas have lesser fleas, and so *ad infinitum*.
And the great fleas themselves, in turn, have greater fleas to go on;
While these again have greater still, and greater still, and so on.

In these words a poet described the activities of the animal world a hundred years ago—and he borrowed from a poet, Jonathan Swift, who wrote the equivalent of the first four lines about two hundred and fifty years ago. So the idea of animals being predators is nothing new to our world.

The dictionary says that the word "predator" comes from a Latin word meaning "plunderer," and that, applied to animals, it means animals that habitually prey on other animals. A recent writer in describing fireflies said that the firefly larva "is a voracious predator," feeding on snails and cutworms. In the same way, dragonflies, eating mosquitoes, are predators; so are the mosquitoes. So are any number of other forms of animal life, large and small, that depend on other animals for food.

However, when someone says "predator," we are likely to think of the larger flesh-eating animals—coyote and wolf, mountain lion, lynx, and bear. These not only eat other animals, but

One of the rarest and most beautiful of our predators is the Canada lynx, a big cat that may grow to more than three feet long.

13

they often eat animals that we would like to protect, especially domestic stock such as pigs, sheep, and cattle. So the term "predator" has come to mean "villain" to us, even though there are hundreds of predators that eat many insects and other animal forms that we are often more comfortable without.

We look philosophically enough at the chain of life when it has to do with a dragonfly swallowing a mosquito, a frog swallowing the dragonfly, a heron gulping down the frog, and an alligator grabbing the heron. But when the last grabber is a coyote after one of our pet lambs, we yell "predator" and reach for the rifle.

When we think about animals, especially if we are trying to learn more about them, our ideas immediately begin to center around "kinds" of animals. But the word "kinds" can be used in many ways. Predators are a "kind" of animal; four-legged animals are a "kind"; animals that lay eggs are a "kind." This little word is so vague that it can be stretched to cover almost anything.

What word is more exact? What can we say when we want to set a mountain lion (for example) apart from a bobcat? They are both *mammals;* they both belong to the cat *family.* Various other animals also fit under both these headings. What heading is more exact for *just* mountain lion; for *just* bobcat?

There are several major branches in nearly every animal family, and each one of these branches is called a *genus.* The genus name is written in Latin, and is always capitalized. The mountain lion belongs to the genus *Felis;* the bobcat belongs to the genus *Lynx.*

But still we do not have a name for *just* the mountain lion, because the ocelot and the jaguar and several other cats belong to the genus *Felis;* the Canada lynx and some others belong to the genus *Lynx.* What we want is a name that will mean, unmistakably, "mountain lion"; unmistakably "bobcat."

What we're doing here, of course, is narrowing each one of these animals down to one exact kind—to a *specific* kind; in other words, to a *species*. And the species has a name. Every animal in the world has a species name that means that specific kind of animal, and no other. The name is in Latin, and it begins with a small letter. It is usually written with the genus name.

Mountain lion? *Felis concolor.* Bobcat? *Lynx rufus.* Gray wolf? *Canis lupus.* Grizzly bear? *Ursus horribilis.* These names

The bobcat, Lynx rufus, *is a different species from the Canada lynx, Lynx canadensis. He is probably a foot shorter, has prominent dark spots, and has only a short wisp of the lynx's big ear tufts.*

are used for these particular kinds of animals, and for no other animals in the world. The other kinds of animals have species names of their own.

Now what is the importance of all this? For one very vital thing, this system of naming provides a way of indexing or listing every form of animal life (and plants too) so that scientists can write about them and people read about them with a minimum of confusion. Common names—coyote, wolf, bear—are fine and are more often used than not. But confusion arises—coyotes are often called "prairie wolves"; there are many different kinds of bears. So when you want to be dead sure that the animal you are reading about is the *specific kind* of animal you think it is, you can check its species name.

Back of all this is a fact about the living world—a fact on which the whole living world turns. It is simply that all the ani-

Our common black bear, Ursus americanus, *may be black, or brown, or cinnamon-colored. These color phases are not separate subspecies.*

mals within a species are very closely like each other; that these animals ordinarily mate with each other and not with animals from another species; and that their young are very closely like them.

Often a group of animals in a species will be a little different from other groups in the same species; this happens most often from one geographic location to another. These subgroups are called *subspecies.* They will usually mate with each other, and they produce young that are like either parent or like both of them. The subspecies name, in Latin, follows the species name: *Felis concolor coryi* is the name of the subspecies of mountain lion that is found in Florida; *Ursus horribilis californicus* is the California grizzly bear.

It is important to understand the difference between a subspecies and a "color phase." Our black bear gives us a common example of color phase, in which cubs of one color may be born to parents of another color. Black, brown, or cinnamon-colored cubs may be born in one litter, and their parents may both be black.

But this does not put the cubs into a separate subspecies. If a subspecies is wiped out, it is gone; no more animals of that subspecies will be born. But if you were to wipe out all the cinnamon-colored bears in the world tomorrow, the next day any number of black mother bears might have cinnamon-colored cubs. And they, throughout their lives, would have black, brown, and cinnamon cubs. There is no such changing back and forth in members of a subspecies.

Now, it is true that if one subspecies is completely wiped out, the species to which it belongs may have another subspecies that is somewhat like it. But the two subspecies are not completely like each other, and no young ever produced by the second subspecies will be exactly like the subspecies that has been lost. When it is gone, it is gone forever. The California grizzly bear, for example, will never be seen again.

How much greater the loss when the last animals of a species are lost! Extinction of a species means that all the animals of all the subspecies have been wiped out. We will never have another passenger pigeon, because all the birds of this species (*Ectopistes migratorius*) died. If our tiny population of whooping cranes is lost, we may still have sandhill cranes (*Grus canadensis*); but they will never give us another whooper (*Grus americana*), even though they belong to the same genus.

How does it happen that a species, or even a subspecies, can be wiped out? Often the answer to this springs from man's ignorance about the living world around him. There is so much of it, and it is so very confusing. A police officer in Louisiana shoots a mountain lion. How is he to know that this may be one of a half-dozen surviving members of a subspecies? Men in a lumbering crew cut down a tree and see a big black and white and red woodpecker fly from it. How are these men to know they have just destroyed one of the few remaining nests of the ivory-billed woodpecker?

Even to scientists, the great array of species and subspecies is a field where knowledge is often lacking and confusion often takes over. It takes a great many well-trained people, working year in, year out, to compile the information we need about this great variety of living things. But the people are at work, and they're working hard, and the results are beginning to come in. Perhaps they will be in time to save many of the species that are threatened today.

THE GRIZZLY BEAR

The grizzly bear is a fine example of an animal that may have many subspecies, and he is a fine example of man's very great confusion regarding them. Some scientists say that there are seventy to eighty subspecies of grizzlies; and even different species. Others say there is probably only one species. Some insist that the giant Alaskan brown bear, largest of all carnivores, is just another kind of grizzly; others that he is an entirely different species—and even that there are several species of the Alaskan brown bear, each distinctly different from the others! One writer thinks that nothing has brought dignified scientists "nearer to name-calling and nose-punching than the question of correctly classifying the grizzly bears."

However they are called, we know that the grizzlies have a great variety of colorings—dark gray, gray, light brownish, tan, yellow; sometimes the ends of the hairs are tipped with silver.

The grizzly, big and powerful though he is, may lose the struggle for survival; some varieties of grizzly have already been wiped out.

From this tipping comes the name, "grizzly," as well as the nick-name, "silver-tip."

And we know, too, that there aren't very many grizzlies left; grizzlies, remember, are predators. Once they were common throughout the plains and westward throughout the mountains. But there are no "Plains grizzlies" today; there are no "California grizzlies." These may have been subspecies or species; so may have a good many other varieties that were wiped out so fast that no scientific description of them was ever made.

We have, today, about 850 grizzlies (that we call *Ursus horribilis*) in Montana, Wyoming, Idaho, and Colorado. Most of them are in Yellowstone and Glacier national parks, where any hunting is illegal. Outside the parks, the states limit hunting or make it illegal at any time. However, only in Alaska is the number of grizzlies actually increasing; in Alaska there are about eleven thousand.

Wherever man lives, he has hunted this animal as a predator, exterminating him with guns, traps, and poison. The grizzly is a big fellow; he may weigh anything from 350 to 850 pounds or more, may be six or seven feet long and stand three and a half feet tall when he is on all fours. He can break a deer's back with one swing of a powerful front paw; and front and hind paws are armed with heavy, straight claws that can rip almost any enemy to pieces. Combine these with sharp teeth and strong jaws, and the very appearance of the grizzly lives up to his scientific name!

So it is no wonder, really, that man does not care for the idea of his lurking around the back yard; and lurk he might, if there were chickens, calves, or even horses to be had for the taking. But he has been wiped out so thoroughly wherever man lives that today the grizzlies live only in deep wilderness—high in mountainous country where man almost never goes. There, he is more afraid of man than man is of him. Usually he goes his own way and minds his own business.

This is largely a business of getting food. He eats any meat that he comes across, including animals he finds dead. He digs ground squirrels and gophers out of the ground, sometimes turning up large areas with those big front claws. During salmon runs, he catches many salmon, and he eats grubs, ants, and bees and their honey. He also eats great quantities of grass, roots, and wild berries.

Grizzlies mate during the summer, and shortly afterward the male and female each goes its own way. They sleep in winter, each in his own den. The female lines hers with leaves, grass, and moss for a soft bed for her cubs. These, usually two, are born in January, helpless and almost naked, and are fed with their mother's milk. By midspring they are big enough to leave the den with her. But they stay with her that summer and the next winter, and perhaps the next one as well.

A mother grizzly has cubs no oftener than every other year, and perhaps only once in three years. She does not have cubs at all until she is three to five years old. The cubs grow very slowly; they do not reach full size until they are seven or eight years old.

So the number of grizzly cubs produced every year is not large, and for a long time they are in danger of attack from mountain lion, coyote, or eagle. But if man, their greatest enemy, will allow them protection in the wilderness, this very interesting kind of animal will probably survive.

THE TIMBER WOLF

From their earliest years, children hear about wolves, in such stories as "Three Little Pigs" and "Red Riding Hood." Always the wolf is the villain of the piece. In grown-up stories, too, a wolf pack trails a lone man on snowshoes or a dog sled, and is held off only by the courageous man's rifle.

Yet, actually, people today have very little contact with wolves. Around the world, man has waged such a war against them that they may become altogether extinct.

The big timber wolf—the gray wolf (*Canis lupus*)—is an animal that was almost wiped out in the United States in the first twenty-five years of this century. There were many subspecies of this wolf, living in most parts of the country, in plains and mountains, in forests and deserts. But by hunting and trapping, by poisoning, by finding the dens and killing the young, by every means he could think of, man has tried to exterminate wolves, and he has nearly succeeded. A very common subspecies, for example, the plains wolf (*Canis lupus nobilis*), became extinct in 1926, even though it was common throughout the Great Plains in earlier years. Even in national parks, where nearly every other animal has been protected, the wolves have been killed.

Alaska is the only one of our states that has many timber wolves today. Here and in Canada, all the way north to Greenland, wolves are fairly numerous, and they are the largest wolves of our times. There are a few wolves near the northern borders of Minnesota, Wisconsin, and Michigan, and they are protected now in these states—the first in history to give protection to wolves. A few found their way across ice or water to Isle Royale National Park in Lake Superior, and so a small pack is protected there. And it is possible that a few continue to live in the deep wildernesses of the Rocky Mountains and perhaps in a few other isolated wilderness localities.

But many subspecies are gone and will never be seen again. You will probably never find a farmer or stockman who will shed tears over that fact, and quite understandably. The timber wolf is powerful and savage, and in the early days of farming and ranching in nearly all parts of this country, he was a hated killer of stock and poultry.

He may stand as much as three feet tall at the shoulders, and weigh well over a hundred pounds. He is heavy and strong, with massive jaws and strong, sharp teeth. And he hunts in packs

Timber wolves may survive man's drive to exterminate them, although some important subspecies have already been wiped out.

whose fighting tactics can bring down a buffalo or a bull moose.

When man moved in, pushing back the elk and moose and killing the buffalo, but bringing cattle and sheep, the wolves found these animals easy to kill. And so began the battle that continued until almost the last wolf was dead.

Yet they are hard to kill, and in their strength and power, they are beautiful animals. From one to another, they vary a great deal in color. Sometimes those in the Arctic are almost white; others are light gray to dark gray, some almost black. Still others are grayish or reddish brown. They are a little like the Arctic sled dogs; in fact, some of the sled dogs are part wolf, and are highly valued for their superior power and endurance.

Without interference from man, wolves live easily in the wild, clubbing together in small packs to pull down fresh meat, and eating all kinds of smaller game—rabbits, rodents of all kinds, any birds they can catch. They mate for life, and seven or more puppies are born in the spring. They have a home den in a cave or hole or under a hollow tree, which is home base for the family until the puppies are eight or ten weeks old. The male wolf helps the mother feed these quick-growing youngsters, bringing fresh meat to them and to her; and he helps her protect them and teach them to hunt for themselves.

Biologists and trappers agree that the timber wolf is one of America's smartest animals. He is a wily hunter, he is hard to trap, and he quickly learns the scent of poison. So if he is given a breathing spell in man's drive against him, a few of his species may be able to survive.

RED WOLF AND COYOTE

Red wolves look so much like coyotes that it is very difficult, looking at them, to tell one from the other. For a long time it was thought that red wolves were much more common than they are, because people thought they were seeing red wolves but were actually seeing coyotes. And far more red wolves have been killed than was intended, because they were mistaken for coyotes.

Yet the two are distinctly different species. The average red wolf is larger than the coyote, and heavier, and redder. With his well-shaped head, big ears, and slender, well-balanced body, he is as beautiful as a handsome dog, and his intelligence matches his beauty.

Once he was common throughout the south from central Texas and Oklahoma eastward, and north to Illinois and Indiana. He has a black color phase that was so common in Florida that it was called "Florida black wolf." But today he is extinct except in a few isolated forest areas, mostly in northeastern Louisiana and western Mississippi. There may be a few—no one knows how many—in southern Louisiana, Texas, Oklahoma, and Arkansas, in the depths of wild forests.

For the red wolf is a forest animal, living on the smaller forest animals that he can catch. Unlike coyotes, which will live close to man and steal his chickens and lambs if given the opportunity, the red wolf draws away from man, deeper into the woods if the woods are still there. As the woods are cut, the coyote moves in and strongly competes for what livelihood remains. So the red

The coyote, smart and strong, seems able to fit his way of life to man's; but as pressure increases on him, he, too, may go.

wolf is crowded out. Today little is known first-hand about red wolves—how many there are, where their dens are, how many young they raise each year. These are facts that must be learned about them if we are to save their species from extinction.

In the opinion of naturalists and biologists, the red wolf is well worth saving, as one of our most interesting and beautiful native animals. The gray wolf probably came to the North American continent from Siberia and Alaska; he is the same species as the gray wolves of Europe and Asia. But the red wolf came into being in North America and is found nowhere else.

What is true of the red wolf is true also of the coyote. He, too, is a native American. But he has withstood the coming of man much more successfully than the red wolf.

Coyotes seem to be able to live anywhere, from farmlands to desert, from plains to mountains. They have even taken up life in small towns and in the outskirts of cities, living on garbage, rats, and mice. They prefer open country to deep woods, and when man moves in and plows a field or herds a band of sheep or raises poultry, the coyote stays around the edges and finds an easy living.

Much of this "easy living" is his natural prey—the rodents that move in too, when man plows and plants. But some of his living is made up of the animals that man is trying to protect—poultry and pigs and lambs.

So here, again, is the predator, with man after him with guns, traps, and poison. Possibly, in spite of all this, the coyote is still outsmarting man and is withstanding the onslaught. He makes use of man. He is often clever enough to avoid poison and traps. And a pair of coyotes have a big brood of five to ten youngsters each year. So the coyote may be holding his own—is, in fact, expanding his range into parts of the country where he was never seen before. But some investigators point to areas where he once was common and now is rare. They count the thousands on thousands of coyotes that have been killed, and predict that this animal, too, will soon be on the endangered list.

SOME PREDATORS OF THE NORTH

There are several kinds of animals living mostly in Canada and Alaska about which we know very little; and we know almost nothing about how many there are of each of these species.

One is the Canada lynx, a beautiful big cat that can live in snowy country and catch rabbits for his food because he has wide, hairy "snowshoes" on his feet, that keep him from sinking into deep snow. He and his mate have, usually, only two kittens each year.

Three others are the wolverine, the fisher, and the marten. These, like the lynx, are wilderness animals, and for food depend on rabbits, squirrels, and other small animals of the wilderness; the wolverine, if he can, steals what may be caught in the traps of man and raids the stores of any cabin that he can break into. In each of these the brood of young is small—from one to four— and the young are not produced every year.

So in all these species, while the living numbers are not known, the chance for survival may be precarious. We know that all of them are seen south of the Canadian border much less frequently today than twenty years ago. Once there were lynxes in the Colorado Rockies, but today they are seldom seen south of Canada, except occasionally in the northernmost parts of Minnesota, Wisconsin, Michigan, and Maine. Martens and fishers were once fairly common along the Pacific Coast, but are not often seen there now. So all of these, too, may be on the endangered list in years to come.

PREDATOR CONTROL

Man has long thought of all these animals as "varmints"— something to be exterminated as quickly as possible. Others are included—foxes and bobcats, eagles and hawks, and various others.

Getting rid of them, called "predator control," has cost him a high price, even if money is all that is considered. Millions of dollars have been paid to hunters and trained exterminators, by the United States government, by various state governments, by counties, by associations of sheep growers and cattlemen. These men, over many years, have been paid to poison, trap, and shoot —to "clean out the coyotes," to "get rid of the varmints." Bounties have been paid in nearly every state on many different kinds of animals—a fixed price for every dead body. In one recent year, one state alone paid bounty on more than twenty-five thousand foxes. Such kills as this have prompted conservationists to brand man himself as the worst predator of all.

Biologists and other researchers have long known that there is a condition in the living world called "the balance of nature." It is a situation very much like that of a seesaw in balance—the seesaw stays level or goes up and down smoothly, within limits. But if someone on one end jumps off suddenly, reducing the weight, that end will fly up and the other end will go down hard!

The balance of nature works in somewhat the same way. In any area, any *habitat*—woods, desert, stream, ocean, or any other —there are many animals that eat other animals and many that eat plants. When a habitat is in balance, there will be enough plants and enough animals to supply those that depend upon them for food; and there will not be enough of any kind of animal to wipe out whatever it uses for food.

But suppose something upsets the balance. Man drains a swamp or cuts a forest or plows a meadow. Or he attempts to control the predators of a habitat. In the preceding chapter, for example, we saw that mountain lions had, for thousands of years, held the deer herds of the Kaibab in balance. Then man got rid of the lions. So the deer end of the seesaw went shooting up, and the plant end came banging down, and the result was almost total disaster.

Coyotes eat sheep, and they also eat ground squirrels and gophers and mice. The sheepmen of a community want the coyotes killed. But a cattleman may say that without coyotes these rodents get to be so numerous that they damage the grazing lands —that their runways on hillsides make the soil wash out and that a whole watershed can then be endangered. Nevertheless, if a sheepman has just had five or six good sheep killed by coyotes, it is difficult to persuade him that there can be anything of value in a coyote's life.

One important thing that man has learned about predator control is that he is running headlong into a problem that looks simple but is actually extremely complex. He may start out to poison a coyote and wind up poisoning a rare California condor. Or he may wipe out the red wolves and bobcats in his neighborhood and find his vegetables ruined by wild pigs. Or he may decide that the sight of a mountain lion in the wild is worth more to him than the lion's keep in deer.

What he learns, and what he decides to do about it, will mean life or death for many of the predators—not only those that are endangered now, but others that he may attempt to "control" as the years go by. The last chapter of this book tells more about what people are doing today to save the predators in danger now, and to keep others off the danger list.

Chapter 3

THE WHOOPERS —
CAN WE SAVE THEM?

When the Ice Age began, probably a million years ago, the North American continent was much as it is today, with great mountain ranges to the east and west and lowlands in the interior. The land was populated with many kinds of giant birds and mammals. Huge mammoths and mastodons and great bisons and camels roamed the plains. Beavers as large as bears lived in the lakes. Wolves and ferocious saber-tooth cats preyed on the other animals, and condors with wingspreads of nine to twelve feet fed on the carcasses of fallen beasts.

Great white cranes searched for food on the wet prairies and along the shorelines. Beautiful swans floated lazily on the water.

During the Ice Age, immense ice sheets from the north moved down into the interior of the continent at least four times, reaching long fingers as far south as the Ohio River and southern Illinois. As the ice sheets advanced, over periods of thousands of years, the birds and mammals slowly retreated toward the south. When the ice melted, they followed its receding edges northward again. Fossil remains of the whooping crane and other cranes, the trumpeter swan, and the California condor and other vultures have been found together in Florida, and, separately or

Whoopers keep a suspicious eye on the photographer while they feed along a beach at Aransas Refuge. When they are not using their wings, the satiny black tips are folded under.

together, in such far-apart places as California and Illinois, Oregon and Kansas, Idaho and Texas.

By the time the last ice sheet had melted from the interior of North America, perhaps ten thousand years ago, most of the giant mammals had disappeared and many of the large birds were also extinct. The wet prairies and many of the swamps and marshes were drying up. Some of the animals that had lived in them and depended on the wetlands for their way of life were able to adjust to the drier conditions. Some were not, and these were crowded into smaller and smaller areas and became fewer and fewer in number.

When the white man came along and "civilized" the New World, wildlife was even more crowded from its natural habitats and slaughtered for food and for skins and feathers. Three of the birds whose fossil remains were found together—whooping cranes, California condors, and trumpeter swans—came dangerously close to extinction; but a few of each still clung precariously to life.

Finally, people began to realize how sad it is when any species of wildlife becomes totally lost to us, and Man the Killer has also become Man the Protector. Through the determined efforts of wildlife-management experts and the support given them by the American public, trumpeter swans are being protected. They have increased until now they are off the danger list, at least for the time being. Many people and organizations are also working hard to save the whooping cranes and the California condors, but the fate of these birds is still uncertain.

People all over the world are interested in the fate of the whooping crane; and the governments of two great nations, the United States and Canada, are cooperating to save it from extinction. The wild whooping cranes winter on and near the Aransas National Wildlife Refuge, on the Texas coast, and migrate in spring to nesting grounds in Canada's Wood Buffalo Park.

It has been estimated that there were no more than fifteen hundred whooping cranes in existence when the white man first came to the New World. Their range probably extended from the Atlantic Coast to Utah and from the Arctic Coast to central Mexico. By 1920 the number of wild whoopers had been cut to about fifty, and by 1941 this had dropped to twenty-one. Since then, they have slowly increased, year by agonizing year. Now there are about seventy whoopers, including those in captivity.

Standing five feet tall, or better, the whooping crane is the tallest native bird in North America. He is a magnificent sight as he paces majestically across his feeding grounds or soars into the

The migration route of the whooping cranes crosses the interior of the United States and Canada, with the Aransas National Wildlife Refuge at the southern end and the nesting site at the northern end.

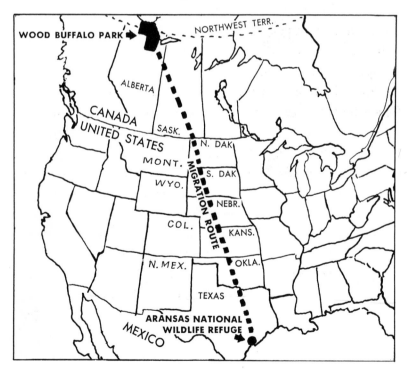

air on great white wings that have a spread of seven feet or more. The adult crane is all white except for satiny black wing tips, carmine-red skin on crown and cheeks, and a "mustache" of stiff black feathers across the cheeks. His neck is long and sinuous, and his slim black legs, which take him over the ground with great speed, are long too.

The female is a trifle smaller than the male and perhaps gentler in bearing, though these differences are hard to see except when a mated pair is together. The young whooper's feathers are brownish in color, gradually turning white during the first year of its life.

Whooping cranes do not migrate in flocks, and early writers who described the "mighty hosts" that filled the skies may have mistaken sandhill cranes for immature whoopers, which they somewhat resemble. The whoopers, however, may have traveled in flocks of twenty-five to fifty in early days, when they were more numerous. Now they usually migrate in pairs or in families —the parent cranes and one, or sometimes two, young—or even singly. And they fly very high, often out of sight. Their clear, bugling call can be heard for miles, and comes from an unusually long windpipe, part of which is coiled inside the breastbone.

In October and November the whooping cranes return from their far northern nesting sites to their winter feeding grounds on the Texas coast. There they feed upon a wide variety of animal and plant life. They eat the small animals that live in or near the water, such as blue crabs, shrimp, small fishes, frogs, marine worms, and water insects. These the cranes dig out of their burrows in the sand, pick off the bottoms of shallow ponds, or probe for with their long bills in the soft mud. They also catch such insects as dragonflies and grasshoppers, and they eat vegetable matter, such as grain and the roots of water plants and acorns.

Whooping cranes mate for life, and the family group stays together for most of the winter. The male parent guards his family and protects the boundaries of his territory. The female feeds the young and teaches it, finally, to feed and take care of itself. The dramatic prenuptial dance of the whoopers begins in late December and continues, at intervals, throughout the winter season.

When the time for spring migration draws near, the cranes become restless, and an air of expectancy hangs over the feeding grounds. Territory limits begin breaking down, and the whoopers wander farther and farther afield. Sometimes they will take to the air, soaring upward in wide circles, as if for the sheer joy of flying, their loud bugling calls ringing out over the marshes. Then down they come, returning to earth in graceful dips and spirals.

Some morning in March or April a family of three, perhaps, will soar into the air, circling higher and higher until they are mere dots in the sky. Their wild, exultant cries become fainter and fainter, until at last they are heard no more. The long northward trek has begun. During the next few weeks, the remaining whoopers, a few at a time, will follow this first daring family to their ancient nesting grounds, a few hundred miles south of the Arctic Circle.

THE ARANSAS NATIONAL WILDLIFE REFUGE

In 1938 there were only two colonies of whooping cranes, totaling twenty-nine, left in North America. Eighteen birds wintered on the Blackjack Peninsula, in Texas, where whooping cranes may have wintered for a million years or more. The peninsula is a broad point of land between San Antonio Bay and St. Charles Bay, northeast of Corpus Christi. The long, narrow Matagorda and St. Joseph islands separate it from the Gulf of Mexico. In December 1937 the Aransas National Wildlife Refuge, containing more than 47,200 acres, had been established on the Blackjack Peninsula to protect the whoopers and many other

kinds of waterfowl that winter there. This Refuge is operated by the Bureau of Sport Fisheries and Wildlife, a division of the U.S. Fish and Wildlife Service.

Another colony of whooping cranes apparently did not migrate in the spring, but lived the year round in almost inaccessible marshes near White Lake, Louisiana. In 1940 there were thirteen birds in this colony, but disaster struck in August of that year. A tremendous storm blew the thirteen cranes inland, away from their marshes, and only six returned after the storm was over. The others had apparently been killed, either by the storm or by hunters. Thereafter this number dwindled, year by year, until only one crane was left at White Lake. Finally, this lone whooper was captured and transferred to the Aransas Refuge, but it lived for only a short time.

Only about ten thousand acres of the Aransas Refuge are suitable feeding grounds for the whoopers. This portion of the Refuge consists of salt flats that lie along the bays separating the Refuge from St. Joseph and Matagorda islands, where there are nearly five thousand additional acres of suitable habitat. The salt

Whooping cranes fly with a slow downbeat and a fast upbeat of the wings. Their long necks are extended, and their legs trail out behind.

Below: In a family group, one of the parent birds is constantly alert, while the other parent and the young are feeding.

flats are three feet or less above sea level and are dotted with shallow, brackish ponds, sloughs, and estuaries, where the whoopers find most of their food.

Recently a 7,162-acre tract of land was donated to the Refuge. The tract lies west of the Refuge, across the upper end of St. Charles Bay. It is not the type of habitat that attracts whooping cranes, however, and will be developed largely for the use of the

rare Attwater's prairie chicken.

Unfortunately, in the spring of 1940, the U.S. Army Engineers cut a channel for the Intracoastal Waterway through the edge of the Aransas Refuge salt flats. The channel used some of the precious acreage, and the Waterway opened the territories of the whooping cranes to a stream of boats and barges. At least one whooping crane has been shot and killed by a marksman on the Waterway and another one crippled.

A STUBBORN WILL TO SURVIVE

Even though he is such a large, striking bird, the wild whooping crane is shy and wary and stays as far away from people as he can. Very little was known about him until the National Audubon Society and the U.S. Fish and Wildlife Service joined forces and set up the Cooperative Whooping Crane Project. Its object was to learn more about the whooper and find ways and means to prevent his extinction.

In the fall of 1946, Robert Porter Allen, Research Director for the Audubon Society, went to Aransas and, with the help of the Refuge staff, began an exhaustive study of the whooping crane. This study lasted several years and covered thousands of miles of travel. Allen prefaced his detailed report of the study with these words:

When you sit crouched in a blind and watch an adult whooper stride close by you, his head high and proud, his bearing arrogant and imposing, you feel the presence of a strength and of a stubborn will to survive that is one of the vital intangibles of this entire situation. Certainly it cannot be overlooked. We have a strong conviction that the whooping crane will keep his part of the bargain and will fight for survival every inch of the way. What are we going to do to help?

Allen's thirteen-year-old son, Bobby, often helped his father with his study of the Aransas whooping cranes. For many hours, Allen and Bobby crouched behind oak brush, trying to catch glimpses of the wary cranes. And they tramped through sticky mud and waded shallow ponds to study the whoopers' feeding habits and learn about their habitat and the territories they set up. Allen found that each family or pair laid out its territory of four to five hundred acres and fiercely defended its invisible boundaries from all other cranes.

As the weeks flew by, Allen still had not been able to observe the cranes close at hand. So he decided to build a blind from which to watch them. He had noticed that the cranes paid no attention to some cattle that fed on the refuge, and he made his blind look as much like a big red bull as he could. It was so realistic that his dog barked at it. So, with high hope, he set it out in a good spot to see cranes and crawled into it before dawn the next morning.

Nothing happened for several hours. Then, as he was swinging his blind around to look out over the salt flats, he saw a horrifying sight! A few yards away a real bull, also red and very large, bore down on him, snorting and pawing the ground. Allen sat frozen, hardly daring to breathe, and stared into the bull's little red eyes. But suddenly the animal turned away, with a bored expression, and went on feeding. Allen's blind may have fooled his dog, but it didn't fool the bull for long!

In early March, Allen left ahead of the whoopers, and checked their migration route through Oklahoma, Kansas, and Nebraska, especially along the Platte River, where the cranes stopped to rest and feed. It was here, too, according to the records, that the greatest number of whoopers had been shot. While Allen was studying the migration route, the assistant biologist at the Aransas Refuge gave full time to checking the departure of the whoopers from the refuge.

By now many citizens of both Canada and the United States were anxious to save the whooping cranes, and people all along the migration route gave Allen much helpful information. He was able to trace the cranes' route northward through the Dakotas and into Saskatchewan, Canada, toward the Great Slave Lake. But there the trail was lost. Although Allen and several other scientists from the United States and Canada flew thousands of miles over northwestern Canada, no sign of the whoopers' nesting sites was discovered.

After a fruitless summer spent searching for the nesting area, Allen returned to Aransas, in time to construct a number of blinds before the whooping cranes came back to the refuge. From one or another of these blinds, placed at strategic points, he was able to watch the returning cranes and learn how they defended their territories and how they cared for their young. Six immature birds and twenty-five adults made the long journey from the north that fall; so there were now thirty-one whoopers on the Texas coast.

Allen learned from observation that pairs of cranes with young were apparently allowed first choice of the territories. Then the pairs without young took the territories that were left, and single birds fed along the edges of the salt flats. The family groups and pairs stayed within their territories most of the time. During a bad storm, they might seek shelter behind nearby patches of oak brush; and, occasionally, they might go to neighboring freshwater ponds for some special food or, in case of drought, for drinking water.

With a pilot from the U.S. Fish and Wildlife Service, Allen spent the next summer flying over northwestern Canada, still hunting the nesting sites of the elusive whoopers, but to no avail. Each year the cranes seemed to drop out of sight. Locating the nesting sites was necessary, because it was important to learn the conditions under which the whoopers were nesting and rearing their young and to insure protection for the nesting area.

Better protection along the migration route was also needed. Allen estimated that seven adult whooping cranes were lost in 1945 to 1949, and the overall gain was twelve. But some hunters in the United States still used the great white birds as targets, and some farmers in Canada still killed them because they thought the cranes were eating their grain. During the years 1950 to 1952, a total of twenty-four adult birds were lost, and the number of wild whoopers again dropped to twenty-one.

The fall migration is especially dangerous for whooping cranes, because that is the hunting season for waterfowl; so hunters were asked not to shoot at *any* large white birds. In September 1953, just before the whoopers were due to start south, the National Audubon Society started a new publicity campaign along the route. Special news releases and announcements were sent to newspapers and to radio and TV stations, films were made available for showing on TV, and educational leaflets were distributed to school children. State game commissions and many other organizations joined with the efforts to save the whoopers.

That year not a single whooper was lost along the route through Canada and the United States!

A forest fire in the summer of 1954 was the occasion for the discovery, at last, of the far northern nesting site of the whooping cranes. A helicopter was returning from the fire, in a remote section of Canada's Wood Buffalo Park. Suddenly the pilot and his passenger spotted two large white birds in a swampy area several miles south of the fire. Flying lower, they realized that the white birds were adult whooping cranes, and with them was their offspring—a small, long-legged, rusty-colored chick. Immediately observations were made from the air by the Canadian Wildlife Service, which confirmed the fact that here was the long-sought nesting area of these great birds.

Word was flashed to the United States, and in 1955 a party of men from Canada and the United States, including Robert Porter Allen, made a difficult and hazardous survey of the area, by plane, helicopter, canoe, and on foot. They spent many weary hours pushing through heavy brush and tramping across wet, boggy ground.

The whoopers could not have found an area more suited to their way of life, or more difficult of access by man! The immense Wood Buffalo Park, containing more than eleven million acres of primitive wilderness, lies across the boundary between Alberta and the Northwest Territories, just south of Great Slave Lake. Here is plenty of space for the large territory that each pair of cranes requires in which to build its nest and rear its young, safe from the encroachment of civilization. No one knows how long whooping cranes have been nesting here.

The area is black spruce swamp and muskeg, dotted with small lakes and ponds that contain food in abundance for the whoopers. The nest is a large, flat mound made of marsh vegetation. Two eggs are laid, but the parents usually succeed in rearing only one chick, though occasionally a family with twins arrives at the Aransas Refuge. It takes about thirty-four days for an egg to hatch but only a day for the chick to gain the use of its legs and be able to run around. When the chick is about two months old, it starts learning to fly; in early October, when it is three months old, it must start the 2500-mile journey to its winter home. By now it has attained the full use of its wings.

THREATS TO THE WHOOPERS

While the Canadians were rejoicing because the whoopers' nesting site had been discovered in their country, an announcement from the United States changed their joy to dismay. The U.S. Air Force has a bombing range on Matagorda Island, and it planned to do some flash-bombing on the island. These flash-bombs are fired at night and light up the countryside for miles around. They frighten away all wildlife, and would probably have been the end of the whooping cranes on Aransas. The U.S. Fish and Wildlife Service and conservationists everywhere, as well as other interests, protested the plan. The Air Force did not give it up, however, until the Government of Canada, urged on by its outraged citizens, made a formal appeal to our State Department.

Later, when plans were being considered to build a branch line of the National Railroad through Wood Buffalo Park to Great Slave Lake, the Canadian Wildlife Service and the Canadian Audubon Society persuaded the railroad to go around the park instead.

Other, less spectacular, dangers constantly threaten the existence of the whooping cranes. Although there are laws against

A whooping crane is fighting another that has invaded his territory. Other kinds of birds, such as the Canada geese in the background, are tolerated.

shooting them, some of the whoopers disappear nearly every year along the migration route. The number of birds is still so small that a devastating storm or a thoughtless man or boy with a gun could reduce them to a new low. Pesticides and radio and TV towers along the way are also threats to the safety of the cranes.

In 1962 the wild whoopers suffered a serious setback. No young were reared that summer, six adults failed to return with the fall migration, and four more adults disappeared during the winter. Since then, however, the number has gradually increased, and the nation rejoiced when ten young birds appeared in the fall of 1964, with the loss of only one adult. The next fall there were eight young birds, but six adults were missing, leaving a total of forty-four wild whoopers. In 1966 the total dropped to forty-three, including five young and thirty-eight adults. So six adults had again been lost. In 1967 the total number rose to forty-eight cranes—thirty-nine adults and nine young—the highest number recorded since the Refuge was established.

For the first time in several years, three whoopers crossed Montana during the 1967 fall migration. When they landed at the Medicine Lake National Wildlife Refuge, all hunting on the waterfowl public hunting area was stopped until they moved on again.

In December one of the adult whoopers wandered off the Refuge and was shot by hunters, who mistook it for a snow goose. Appalled at what they had done, the hunters took the crane to the authorities at the Refuge, who rushed it to a veterinarian at San Antonio. But the bird was so badly wounded that it could not be saved.

Because of the deep interest in the whoopers, many people go to the Aransas Refuge to see them. To keep the very shy cranes from becoming frightened and leaving the refuge, their feeding grounds have been closed to the public. However, an observation tower in a clump of trees gives a good view of the grounds, and a private boat takes tourists along the Intracoastal Waterway. Fortunately, boats do not seem to disturb the cranes.

CAN THE WHOOPERS BE SAVED?

If the size of the flock continues to increase, even as slowly as at present, the Aransas Refuge may soon be too small for it. As a result of his study, Robert Porter Allen advised enlarging the Refuge, including at least some of Matagorda and St. Joseph islands. The National Audubon Society has leased nearly six thousand acres on Matagorda Island from a private owner and has stationed a vigilant warden there to protect the whoopers that winter in the area.

Allen also suggested the establishment of one or more national refuges along the Platte River, where the whoopers could feed during migration. The cranes lost a good friend when Allen died in 1963.

In an effort to keep the cranes from wandering off the Refuge in search of food, two hundred-acre plots of land on the Aransas Refuge have been fenced and planted to grain sorghum and other kinds of grain. The whoopers use these areas quite heavily. When they have eaten all the standing crop, supplementary feedings of grain are spread on the ground.

Other studies and experiments are under way or are being planned by the Refuge staff in a continuing effort to improve the wintering grounds, so that more birds can be taken care of as the number of whoopers increases. One of the experiments under construction is a man-made fifty-acre tidal pool, where the whoopers can find the kind of sea food they like. Water from the Gulf will be pumped into the pool—water that contains hundreds of small sea animals, such as crayfish, blue crabs, shrimp, and small fish. If this pool proves successful, other pools will be built.

The whooping cranes, themselves, appear to be changing some of their habits, and their territories are not as large or as well defined as they once were—often only two hundred acres or less. Furthermore, observers at the Refuge frequently see ten to twenty birds feeding in an area no more than five hundred acres in size. Sometimes as many as thirty whoopers eat together in the hundred-acre plots.

Some people feel that the dangers to the wild whooping cranes are so great that they cannot be saved from extinction. They think that some of the cranes, at least, should be caught and held in captivity instead of being allowed to make the long, dangerous journey twice a year between Aransas and Wood Buffalo Park. The National Audubon Society and other conservationists are opposed to this on the grounds that attempts to capture any of the birds might easily cause injury to some and scatter the others beyond recall. Besides, whoopers caged in zoos are no substitute for the wild ones, free to stake out their territories or wing their way through the sky to their far nesting sites. The Society feels that it would be better to try to improve the wild cranes' habitat and give them as much protection as possible.

Attempts to breed whooping cranes in captivity have been going on for some years. A wounded crane, found in Louisiana in 1940, was taken to the Audubon Zoo in New Orleans and named Josephine. Apparently she was one of those that had disappeared in the storm at White Lake, Louisiana.

Later, Josephine was loaned to the Aransas Refuge and mated with a crippled male whooper called Crip. When their chick, Rusty, hatched in April 1950, the news of the first whooping crane to be hatched in captivity was headlined in every newspaper in this country and Canada. Unfortunately, Rusty disappeared when he was four days old, probably caught by a raccoon or crow.

When Josephine was returned to the New Orleans Zoo, Crip went with her, and in 1957 the pair finally succeeded in hatching and rearing twin offspring. They were given the names George

Above: An unhatched whooping-crane chick is using the sharp point on its bill to break through the eggshell. Right: This sturdy little whooping crane was hatched from an egg flown to the Patuxent Research Center from the Canadian nesting site.

and Georgette, but both proved to be males. In later years, two single chicks—Pepper, a male, and Pewee, a female—were hatched and reared. Josephine, who had become an international celebrity, died from shock a few days after Hurricane Betsy smashed through New Orleans in 1965.

A crippled female whooper, injured on her way north, was found in Texas and loaned to the San Antonio Zoo by the U.S. Fish and Wildlife Service. She was named Rosie and kept at the zoo for several years. Then, in 1964, she was sent to the New Orleans zoo to mate with George, in the hope that they would rear more cranes in captivity. However, the pair did not nest, and in January of 1967 Rosie was mated with Crip, widower of Josephine.

The two cranes were brought back to the San Antonio Zoo, where Rosie laid two eggs in June, which hatched in July. The first chick to hatch apparently was trampled to death or smothered by its mother when only a day old. So the second chick, hatched three days later, was taken from the parents, to be reared by hand. Later, this chick was moved to the Patuxent Research Center, of the Bureau of Sport Fisheries and Wildlife, at Laurel, Maryland.

Another captive whooper is Canus, whose wing was so badly crippled that it had to be amputated. Apparently injured at the nesting site when he was learning to fly, Canus was rescued in September 1964 by the Canadian Wildlife Service and flown to a U.S. Fish and Wildlife Service research center at Monte Vista, Colorado. Later he was moved to the Patuxent Center, where he now has his full adult plumage and is a beautiful and stately bird.

Also at the Patuxent Center, an interesting experiment is going on with captive cranes. For six years the center worked with varieties of sandhill cranes, which are closely related to the whoopers, in order to learn how to rear cranes in captivity. Eggs were removed from the nests of wild sandhill cranes and transported to the center, where they were hatched in incubators. The young chicks were fed and reared by hand.

A plan had been worked out earlier with the Canadian Wildlife Service to take eggs from the wild whooping-crane nests and fly them to Patuxent, where the chicks would be hatched and reared in captivity. In the spring of 1967 the Canadian Wildlife Service and the Bureau of Sport Fisheries and Wildlife decided the time was right to put the plan into action.

On June 2 a team of Canadian and U.S. scientists were flown by helicopter to the whoopers' nesting site. Seven nests, six of them with two eggs each, had previously been located by the Canadian Wildlife Service observers, and six eggs were taken, one from each of the six nests. Later, an additional nest with two eggs was discovered.

Although two eggs are usually laid, the parents are seldom able to rear more than one chick. Based on the studies of the sandhill cranes, the scientists hoped that, if they took just one egg from each nest, the parent cranes would be able to hatch and rear the other chick and there would be no loss because of the experiment. This proved to be sound thinking, because nine young whoopers returned in October to Aransas from the northern nesting site.

The six eggs were placed in a portable incubator and flown to the Patuxent Center. One egg started to hatch on the way, and the chick died in the shell. The other eggs hatched normally, but one young bird developed a weakness of the "knee" joints about ten days after it hatched. This condition worsened until the bird died at the age of two months. One other young bird showed a similar difficulty with one leg, but the crane has continued to grow and the condition may eventually be corrected by surgery. The remaining three birds are fine specimens, with fully developed wing and body plumage.

Encouraged by this success, scientists again went to the nesting site on June 1, 1968, and took nine eggs and one chick from the whooping-crane nests. A second chick hatched from one of the eggs, and the two chicks and remaining eggs were flown to the Patuxent Center, where all the eggs hatched. Secretary of the Interior Stewart L. Udall called the project "a major success in man's battle to preserve this rare bird."

On later flights over the nesting site, eight young whoopers were seen with their parents, but the total number could not be tallied until after the return of the whooping cranes to Aransas in the late fall.

Conservationists hope that the young whoopers at Patuxent will be the start of a captive flock, whose offspring can be used to increase the number of wild whooping cranes.

Chapter 4

THE CHANGE-NOTS

"A living fossil!" some people call the California condor. "A relic of the Ice Age!"

"It soars over California as a giant shadow from the past," says one writer.

In the Ice Age there were many of these great birds. They fed on the carcasses of fallen giant mammals and ranged, apparently, from Florida to California. But times changed, and the condors could not keep up with the changes. So they withdrew into the high mountain wildernesses of the far West, and their numbers became fewer and fewer.

Where there is a change in the conditions for which a species is fitted, the species must either adapt, move on, or die. Many species, like the California condor, have been unable to adapt to the rapidly changing conditions caused by the coming of man. Some of these have already become extinct. Others, such as the condor, the Kirtland's warbler, and the Everglade kite, have withdrawn into smaller and smaller habitats and are threatened with extinction. Now man is attempting to provide suitable living conditions for these endangered species so that they will continue to exist and to perpetuate their kind.

THE CALIFORNIA CONDOR

In the early 1800s, condors ranged as far north as the lower

The Kirtland's warbler does not nest unless it can find a grove of young jack pine.

51

Columbia River, and were mentioned in the journals of Lewis and Clark and in other writings of that period. The condors apparently did not nest north of San Francisco, however. Today their range is confined almost entirely to several southern counties in California, north and northwest of Los Angeles. Most of the nesting sites and the principal winter roosting areas are in the high cliffs and mountain slopes of two sanctuaries in the Los Padres National Forest—the Sespe Wildlife Area and the Sisquoc Condor Sanctuary.

The California condor, with a wingspread of eight and a half to nine and a half feet and weighing twenty pounds or more, is North America's largest soaring bird and one of the world's rarest birds. When we see it hunched on a perch or waddling awkwardly on the ground, we can understand why some authorities claim that it is a "senile species," on its way out. Its dark plumage, small, bald orange head, and heavy beak give it a grotesque, "other-world" appearance. But in the sky it is a different bird! Now we can appreciate its grace and beauty as it soars high above us, the sun flashing from the large white patches under its wings when it wheels and turns.

The condor can glide in a straight line for many miles, without having to flap its wings. Because of this, it is sometimes mistaken for an airplane. For such flights, however, it must have the right air currents. It uses thermals—ascending air currents caused by the sun's heat—or the upcurrents on the windward side of a ridge or mountain slope, to spiral upward in wide circles until it is high enough to glide. It is, in truth, a living sailplane.

Because of its heavy weight, the condor cannot take off directly from a flat surface but must run for several yards into the wind before launching itself into the air. So, when it alights on the ground to feed, it must have plenty of unobstructed space in which to take off again. When perching, it selects a dead limb on a tall tree or the edge of a cliff, from which it can fly with ease.

It is hard to believe that this grotesque-looking California condor, perched on the edge of a cliff, is sometimes mistaken for an airplane when he soars on graceful wings high above the earth.

Condors return to roost every night in the same area, where they can perch high above the ground. They prefer to roost in conifers with large, dead limbs that do not sway in the wind, because a condor's toes cannot grasp the perch firmly. The roosting trees must be on high slopes or above cliffs, so that the condors will have a long, downhill sweep when they take off.

Sometimes they roost on the cliffs themselves, especially near nesting sites or waterholes.

Most nesting sites are in cavities in the sides of cliffs or among boulders, although one condor nest was found in a hollow sequoia tree. Caves are favorite spots for nesting sites, but there must be suitable perching spots nearby for the parent condors—trees or cliffs—as well as room for them in the cave.

The female condor does not begin to lay eggs until she is five or six years old, and then she lays only one egg every other year. However, if the egg does not hatch or the chick does not survive, she may lay again, either that same year or the next. There is no real nest; the egg is laid in the sand or dirt on the floor of the cave and takes about forty-two days to hatch. The parent birds take turns incubating the egg and brooding the chick, as well as feeding it.

The chick is practically helpless when it first hatches, and it gains strength slowly. It stays close to the spot where it was hatched for about three weeks and does not leave the nesting site until it is at least five months old. Even then it cannot fly, but must perch on nearby cliffs or trees for some weeks more; it cannot soar with adult condors until it is nine to eleven months old. Its parents continue to feed it, sometimes into the second summer. The young condor has a dark-gray head, and the white patches under the wings are mottled with brown. It does not attain full adult plumage until it is five or six years old.

Condors will feed upon the carcasses of some domestic animals —calves, sheep, and, occasionally, horses and cows—and they have been known to feed within sight of houses and barns and other buildings if people were not visible. But with man himself, they will have no dealings. And who can blame them, for he has proved to be their worst enemy—indeed, practically their only enemy!

Although the condor is a scavenger and does no one any harm

—he has never been known to attack a living mammal—this big bird has been harassed and killed since prehistoric times. The Indians used him in their religious ceremonies. The early-day California miners stored their gold dust in his quills. Collectors stole condor eggs, took the chicks from the nests, and shot the parents in order to sell them to museums and zoos and to other collectors. In our own time, hunters shoot condors just for the doubtful "fun" of killing something, although, for many years, California laws have forbidden killing or molesting these birds.

To the contention that the condor has "outlived its time" and "its doom is near," the National Audubon Society says not so! Given half a chance, it can increase its numbers and continue to enrich America's wildlife resources. With this hope, state and federal governments, as well as many organizations and individuals, are working together in a determined effort to save the condors.

Little was known about the condor until the National Audubon Society, with the aid of the University of California and the United States Forest Service, made two detailed studies, the second of which was financed by the National Geographic Society. The first study, made in the late 1940s, counted at least sixty condors and disclosed much about their habits. By the time the second study was made, in the early 1960s, the number had dropped to about forty.

When a careful two-day count was made in October 1965 by four agencies—the California State Fish and Game Department, the U.S. Forest Service, the U.S. Bureau of Sport Fisheries and Wildlife, and the National Audubon Society—only thirty-eight condors could be found. It was evident to everyone that drastic steps must be taken at once if this unique species was to be saved from extinction.

The California legislature passed a law doubling the penalty for taking, killing, or injuring a condor. Anyone convicted of violating this law can now receive a thousand-dollar fine or a year in jail or both. The National Audubon Society appointed a full-time warden; the state game wardens gave special attention to protecting the condors; and the U.S. Forest Service stepped up patrols to keep the nesting and roosting areas in the Los Padres National Forest free from disturbances.

Protection for the nesting areas is especially important, because the appearance of a person within five hundred yards of a nest, or a loud noise a half mile or more away, can cause the parent birds to stay away from the nest for twenty-four hours or more and sometimes to desert it entirely. So visitors are not permitted near the nesting sites, and road and trail building are kept as far from such sites as possible.

Protection of the adult birds is difficult because condors range thirty to forty miles from the sanctuaries in the national forest and often feed on private land. The help of private citizens is the great need here, and so the California Fish and Game Department and the National Audubon Society cooperated in an educational campaign to tell all the people in the state about this great bird and enlist their interest in saving him from extinction. These two organizations published several leaflets telling about the condor and the great danger he was in, and distributed them widely, both in the schools and to the general public. The Santa Barbara Audubon Society and other California societies helped with the campaign, and articles were published in state and national magazines.

All these workers had their reward and the rejoicing was great when the second annual condor count showed fifty-one of the giant birds, thirteen more than the year before. All thirteen probably were not the young of that year; some may have been overlooked in the census of the year before. After all, it isn't easy to count birds that are so shy and have such a wide soaring range.

But apparently no birds were lost during the year, and the increase shows that the condors are able to hatch and rear their young. Short of a major disaster, they are not on the way out.

Such a disaster, however, from time to time has threatened the condors in the Sespe Wildlife Area, and still hangs over them. This threat is known as the Sespe Creek Project and involves erecting two dams on Sespe Creek, one of which, with its reservoir, would be on the north edge of the Sespe sanctuary. Even worse, a road would be constructed through the heart of the sanctuary. The Sespe Creek Project is the brain child of the U.S. Bureau of Reclamation, whose job it is to get water where it is needed, rather than to preserve wildlife resources or scenic beauty. The project is being pushed by business interests in the area but is opposed by all the conservation organizations that have been working so hard to save the condors. It is also opposed by the U.S. government bureaus that are charged with guarding our wildlife. Fortunately for the condors, the taxpayers in the area voted against the project in March 1966.

The U.S. Forest Service and the U.S. Bureau of Sport Fisheries and Wildlife have joined forces in the campaign to keep this giant bird from becoming extinct. Their efforts include a study of the effects of poisons used in predator and rodent control to determine whether such poisons are a threat to condors. The Forest Service plans to enlarge the sanctuaries and to keep disturbances of all kinds away from them.

Several captive South American condors, a different species but similar to their California cousins, are being observed at the Patuxent Wildlife Research Center, at Laurel, Maryland, for the purpose of obtaining information that may help to save our condors. With so many forces working in behalf of this great bird, he may long outlive the dire prophecies of his doom and continue soaring high above his California mountains.

THE KIRTLAND'S WARBLER

The Kirtland's warbler is a good example of a species with very special habitat requirements. Each May this little blue-gray, black, and yellow warbler migrates from its winter home in the Bahama Islands to Michigan's "jack-pine barrens," which are located in about twelve counties in the north-central section of the Lower Peninsula. The whole nesting range is about one hundred miles long by sixty miles wide. It is centered on Crawford and Oscoda counties and drained by the Au Sable River.

Many other birds like to nest in the jack-pine thickets, but they don't insist on this environment. If jack pines are not available, they will nest just as happily in other woods. But not the Kirtland's warblers! They must not only have jack pines, but young jack pines, six to twenty feet tall, that cover an area of at least eighty acres. The warblers nest on the ground under the thick, low branches of the pines, and when the trees grow so tall that these low branches begin to die or to become straggly, the birds move on to another thicket.

The male Kirtland's warbler perches on the limb of a tree in the area of the nest and sings loudly, wagging his tail up and down all the while. Between songs, he brings juicy caterpillars to his mate on the nest. When the young birds hatch, both parents are kept busy feeding them.

The entire Kirtland's warbler population is probably less than a thousand, which isn't very many, when we consider the many dangers that threaten this little bird. One of the greatest threats is loss of the only habitat in which it can, or will, nest.

Strange as it may seem, the factor which has been most important in saving this warbler from extinction is one that is most terrifying to other wildlife—the forest fire. Most of the cones of the jack pine open and scatter their seeds only under extreme heat; natural stands of young jack pine spring up after forest fires burn over areas where jack pines were present. In recent years, however, forest fires have been so well controlled that thickets of young jack pines have become fewer and fewer.

About ten years ago, the state of Michigan set aside three tracts of land, totaling nearly seventy-seven hundred acres, on which to set up proper nesting sites for the warblers; several years later the U.S. Forest Service added a four-thousand-acre area of Huron National Forest to the project. The Forest Service decided to use nature's way, burning, but very carefully controlled burning. The area has been divided into twelve units; every five years, one of these units will be burned over, after the large trees have been logged. This will insure that there will always be young stands of jack pines for the warblers to nest in when the trees in their former nesting sites become too large. The first burnings, called "Operation Pop-cone" by the Forest Service, have been reasonably successful.

An unusual threat to Kirtland's warblers is the recent invasion of the cowbird into their nesting range. Instead of building its own nest and rearing its young, the cowbird lays its eggs in other birds' nests, one or more to a nest. Then the other birds hatch the eggs and rear the young. The cowbird nestling is usually much larger than the young of the birds that built the nest. So it gets most of the food, and the other nestlings are too weak to survive. Sometimes the young cowbird pushes the other little birds from the nest. Plans are being studied to control the cowbird population and protect the young Kirtland's warblers.

Many citizens and organizations, including the Michigan Audubon Society and the Detroit and Pontiac Audubon societies, are interested in preserving the Kirtland's warbler. Very little is known about its wintering grounds in the Bahamas, but the Florida Audubon Society is trying to get protection for it in the areas where it has been seen.

THE EVERGLADE KITE

Like the wood stork and much other wildlife in Florida, the Everglade kite depends upon fresh-water ponds and marshes for his feeding grounds. But he is different from many of the others because he eats one thing and one thing only—a species of snail that lives in fresh water.

The limpkin, for example, is another Florida bird of pond and marsh, and he eats the same kind of snail. But he eats many other things, too—crayfish and lizards and frogs, insects and worms. But the Everglade kite goes hungry if there are no snails of his particular kind.

"Green" snails (also called "apple" snails) live in shallow fresh water and climb out on grass or lily pads. The kite, a kind of hawk, flies low and swoops one up in his claws. He lights in a nearby bush or hummock and digs the snail out of its shell with his sharply curved bill, a tool that seems to have been especially made for this very purpose. Then he goes in search of another snail.

Before draining began in Florida, Everglade kites were common in all the fresh-water marshes. Today there may be fewer than fifty birds, most of them in the Loxahatchee National Wildlife Refuge in southeastern Florida; some have been seen along the Tamiami Trail. In one year, only ten were counted. There are other subspecies of these kites in Mexico, South America, and Cuba. But these few are all that remain of Florida's kite.

There are many other areas in Florida where the green snail is abundant, but the kites have gone. They have been shot by hunters, and fire and drought may have combined to wipe them out. When so few were left, they could not come back to areas that might well support them.

A pair of kites raises only one family in a year, and the family usually has no more than two young birds. If the nests are disturbed in any way, the kites may desert them. So the nests at

With its number estimated at about fifty, Florida's Everglade kite may be increasing. Observers protect it by taking great care not to disturb it.

Loxahatchee are carefully guarded, and not even observing naturalists can study the nesting birds, for fear of frightening them away.

But there, it is hoped, the number of birds will slowly increase until they can spread out to other areas and once more be seen as part of Florida's wildlife.

Chapter 5
TARGETS ALL

From the time that the white men of Europe discovered and began to settle the North American continent, they hunted animals with guns. Before that, Indians hunted them with bow and arrow and with devices that threw rocks.

Hunting, as a matter of fact, occupied a great deal of the lives of Indians and of early white men. The game and fish that they could bring to the dinner table often decided whether they were well-fed or hungry. Indians hunted buffalo not only for food but for hide, bone, and sinew, wasting none of it. White men could never have settled and developed the land without the wild animals that gave them meat and furs.

Then, as more and more white people came to this continent and brought with them roads and railroads, farms and factories, there came a great change in the source of man's food. Food became something that was grown in a garden, or raised on a cattle ranch, or bought in a store.

So did man hang up his guns? Did they become an oddity, for which there was no longer any use, like a spinning wheel or a churn? Hardly! Instead, they became better every year, easier to handle, more deadly. Man had discovered that hunting was fun, and so sport hunting was off to a flying start.

Today, hunting and fishing for sport are world-wide, and the

This little key-deer fawn was only twenty-five days old when its picture was taken. It measured fourteen and a half inches tall at the shoulder and weighed six pounds.

money spent for them runs into billions of dollars. Guns and ammunition, fishing equipment, camping equipment, special clothing, sports magazines filled with advertising—these make up a vast industry that has grown up around the sportsman.

In the light of all this, you may think it a wonder that there are any animals left. And so we come to a very strange fact: In spite of all the sportsmen's guns aimed at animal life, they have almost never caused, by themselves, the extinction of any kind of animal, or even brought it to such low numbers that it was endangered!

 It is true that most of the endangered species and the extinct species have at some time been a target for the sportsman. But in almost every case, there has been some other element at work along with the sportsman's gun. Sometimes, as with the passenger pigeon, it has been market shooting. Sometimes, as with the mountain lion, it has been predator control. Often, as with the whooping crane, it has been destruction of habitat. Then, sport shooting could be the final blow necessary to destroy the species.

But in general, the sportsman is a good conservationist. He knows he has to be, or there will soon be nothing for him to hunt. He, along with others, is learning to recognize the danger signals, and to call a halt to hunting animals that are threatened. So there are hunting laws now in every state to protect some of the rare animals. For example, not so long ago the beautiful pronghorn antelope of the West was threatened with extinction. So hunting was stopped on it altogether, and it was encouraged to move into areas where it would have plenty of food and protection. Today, Colorado estimates that there are more than twenty-five thousand pronghorns in that state alone; and there are open hunting seasons there and in other states where this animal has prospered.

The true sportsman is beginning to look at rare wildlife in a different light. Once he could shoot a rare animal and bring it in

When it was threatened, the pronghorn responded so well to protection that today it is an important big-game animal.

and hang it on his wall as a mark of honor. But now it may mark him as a law-breaker; certainly it will mark him as a killer of something that other men are trying to save.

There are, however, hunters who are far from being real sportsmen. They shoot for the pleasure of killing, and they shoot at anything alive. Such a man, when hunting deer where the law allows him only one, may shoot one and let it lie, so that he can go on to shoot another. Some men in a boat in Florida rode down the middle of a narrow bay and shot every sea gull they saw perched on posts on each side of it. Men have shot at the almost extinct California condor and whooping crane. These hunters, of course, are only a few among the many good sportsmen. But their guns are deadly, and they can make the difference between whether a species survives or is destroyed.

THE POLAR BEAR

The white bear of the North is an animal that is seriously threatened by bad sportsmanship in hunting. He has solved the problems of living in a most unfriendly habitat. He has no enemies in the animal world except man. Yet man's guns are threatening to exterminate him.

The polar bear lives in the Arctic, in all the countries that circle the North Pole. But he seldom lives far inland, on the land itself. His usual home is the ice pack of the Arctic, riding along with it as it breaks up, floats apart, forms again, freezes, melts, and freezes again. He swims for miles in open water to go from one ice floe to another. He rides the ice down "iceberg alley" from northern Greenland, then may travel overland to reach the northward-floating ice pack again. But he never leaves open water for long, because in open water is his food supply.

His food is almost entirely seals. They come out of the water to bask on the ice, and he stalks them, slipping slowly, slowly closer, almost invisible because of his white coat.

Polar bears mate in the summer, then separate. The male bear does not hibernate, but stays abroad through the whole dark winter, when the Arctic knows no sun. In the middle of the winter, the female digs deep into a ridge of piled-up ice and makes a snug den, soon sealed off by ice and snow. Here, early in the spring, she gives birth to two tiny cubs, hairless, blind, completely helpless. Many weeks go by before she can bring them out of the den. Then they stay with her for many months —through that summer and the next winter, before they are able to shift for themselves. So cubs are born to a mother polar bear, not every year, but every other year.

Regardless of where they are born, or where the seals are thickest, the polar bears are scattered far and wide by the shifting of the ice. They move from the territorial waters of one country to another, and so "belong" to no country. Worse, they move

A mother polar bear keeps her cubs with her for more than a year after their birth. This picture was taken from a U.S. Coast Guard helicopter.

into international waters, and so can be protected by no country.

International conferences have been held to arrive at some way to protect the bears. All of the countries in the Arctic are agreed that they should be protected. But hunters who are not stopped by feelings of sportsmanship can still kill them, and are killing them. These men hire airplanes to take them beyond territorial waters and over international waters where any country's laws do not reach. They fly low over the ice until they find a bear. Then they land alongside and shoot it.

Authorities estimate that there are from eleven to twelve thousand polar bears in the Arctic, and that they are being killed at the rate of about twelve hundred per year. Some of these are killed by Eskimos, who need them for food and fur. But the number killed by "sportsmen" is increasing each year. So it is feared that the day is not far off when polar bears in zoos will be the only ones alive.

THE ESKIMO CURLEW

During the fall and spring migration seasons, vast flocks of shore birds—willets and snipes, the golden plover and the Eskimo curlew, and many others—once filled the skies and were an amazing wildlife spectacle. Unfortunately they were also a fine target for market hunters and sportsmen, who slaughtered them in such numbers that they were almost exterminated before the end of the last century. Finally, laws were passed in Canada and the United States that saved the golden plover and other shore birds from complete extinction. But protection may have come too late for the dainty little Eskimo curlew.

Smallest of the North American curlews, the Eskimo curlew is only about twelve inches long. It has a shorter, much thinner bill than other curlews, and the bill is only slightly curved. This bird is a rather dark buffy brown, with a lighter breast and cinnamon brown on the underside of the wings.

The Eskimo curlews nested and reared their young on the barren tundras of Canada, west of Hudson Bay. In late July they left their nesting sites and flew to Labrador, on Canada's east coast, where they fattened on snails and crowberries, sometimes called curlew berries.

Then the curlews crossed the Gulf of St. Lawrence to Nova Scotia and from there started their long, nonstop flight to the coast of South America. Sometimes storms at sea blew them inland, and they were forced to spend a few days along the New England coast. But finally they arrived at their faraway wintering grounds at the southern tip of Argentina, eight thousand miles from their nesting sites. In the spring they returned by way of the Texas coast and the prairie states west of the Mississippi.

Golden plovers often shared the curlews' nesting grounds and made the long flight with them to South America. It is believed that these birds—Eskimo curlews and golden plovers—are the ones that flew in large numbers over the ships of Christopher Columbus and guided him to land. Authorities say that they are the only birds strong enough and swift enough to make this long nonstop flight across the ocean.

After the New World became settled and "civilized," the Eskimo curlews were slaughtered by the thousands wherever they appeared, in Canada, South America, and the United States. Their habit of fattening before they started on their long journey from or to Canada made them a table delicacy. They were gentle, trusting birds, not easily frightened by the approach of the gunners, and many of them could be killed with one shot. In the 1870s and '80s, wagonloads were killed and sent to the markets in the big cities. Sometimes they were killed just for "sport" and left in great piles, to rot or be eaten by pigs or other animals.

By the time laws were passed to stop the killing, very few were left. For years scientists believed that the Eskimo curlew was extinct, until, in 1945, a pair was sighted in Texas. No more were seen until the spring of 1959, when one, and possibly more, appeared in Texas. After that, each year from 1960 to 1966, at least one Eskimo curlew was seen in Texas. Since the bird was seen by a number of people at different times and at different places, it is uncertain whether it was always the same bird or different birds.

In September 1963 a lone Eskimo curlew was shot by a hunter on the island of Barbados, and its skin is now in the Philadelphia Academy of Natural Sciences.

THE KEY DEER

The story of the Key deer has a happier ending than that of the Eskimo curlew. This tiny deer is a subspecies of the white-tailed deer, but it is less than half the size of its northern relatives. In fact, it is no larger than a good-sized setter or collie dog. It can weigh as little as forty pounds and stands about twenty-eight inches tall at the shoulder. It is also paler in color than the large white-tails.

The Key deer once ranged over most of the keys, or islands, of southern Florida, swimming from key to key in search of food and fresh water. Now they are found only on about a dozen keys in Monroe County, centered by Big Pine Key and bearing such intriguing names as Cudjoe Key, Knockemdown Key, Big Torch Key, and Little Spanish Key.

The tule elk, like the Key deer, are a dwarf subspecies, very rare, and in

It is hard to understand how man could hunt these elfin creatures with dogs and kill them with guns and fire—but kill them he did, wantonly and without mercy. By the late 1940s, there were only about thirty of them left.

Finally the Florida Game and Fresh Water Fish Commission and the U.S. Fish and Wildlife Service publicized the plight of the tiny deer. Then several wildlife conservation organizations, including the National Wildlife Federation, the Boone and Crockett Club, the Wildlife Management Institute, and the National Audubon Society, went to their aid. Wardens were hired to patrol the Key deer range and keep people from killing them, and money was raised to buy seventeen acres for a refuge. Stories were published in newspapers and magazines, such as the *Audubon Magazine*, so that people all over the country could learn about the deer.

Bills were introduced in Congress to establish a National Key Deer Refuge. The bills were backed by the Florida Game Commission and the U.S. Fish and Wildlife Service, but they were opposed by local land developers, who wanted to build houses on the Key deer range. Through the efforts of the National Wildlife Federation, the National Audubon Society and local Audu-

need of protection if they are to survive.

bon societies, and many other organizations and private citizens, the bill was finally passed in 1953 to establish the National Refuge. As fast as possible, the U.S. government acquired title to more than seven hundred and sixty acres, partly by direct purchase and partly by donations from organizations and private land owners. Other tracts, totaling fifty-three hundred acres, were leased for the Refuge.

The Key deer responded to all these efforts by increasing to around three hundred in little more than a decade; they now number about four hundred.

The threat of being crowded from their habitat by land developers still hangs over the tiny deer, because much of the land under lease is for short terms only. The owners can terminate the leases whenever they want to. However, the National Audubon Society has purchased seven hundred and fifty acres of prime habitat, some of it practically from under the blades of the developers' bulldozers, and leased it to the Refuge.

A bill was passed by Congress in 1966 to remove the limitation of one thousand acres which could be acquired for the Refuge. The bill also authorized more than two million dollars to be spent for additional land.

A number of Key deer are killed each year on U.S. Highway 1—the Overseas Highway—which crosses the keys just south of the Refuge. But in spite of the dangers from hurricanes and forest fires and death on the highway, the future looks bright for these little deer.

THE TULE ELK

Across the continent from Florida is another dwarf species that is in trouble. The tule elk of California, like the Key deer, has been killed without mercy and crowded from his habitat by man. This elk is similar to the Rocky Mountain elk except that it is smaller and paler in color. It is named for the water plants, called tule, that grow thick in the marshes where it took refuge.

The tule elk was once plentiful in California's San Joaquin and Sacramento valleys, but it was slaughtered in such numbers during the Gold Rush days that it almost became extinct. Only a very few—no one knows just how many—were left in the tules. Fortunately a farsighted rancher named Henry Miller protected a few of the elk on his ranch in Kern County; and in 1873 a state law was passed making the killing of a tule elk a felony.

By 1914 the elk herd had grown to about four hundred animals, and they were causing so much damage to the alfalfa fields in the area that portions of the herd were sent to other areas in the state. None of these transplants was very successful, however.

The fenced 953-acre California Tule Elk Reserve State Park, southwest of Bakersfield, supports thirty-five elk, but supplemental feedings of hay pellets are required. Another herd of about eighty elk roams the Cache Creek area, northwest of Sacramento.

In 1933 tule elk were introduced into Owens Valley, which is a long, narrow valley between the Sierra Nevada, on the west, and the Inyo Mountains on the east. Here, on range land, the elk must compete for food with domestic livestock. Fortunately elk are to some extent browsing animals—that is, they eat leaves and twigs of woody plants that cattle ordinarily do not eat.

So the tule elk in Owens Valley flourished and their numbers increased until the state allowed hunting, to hold them to not more than three hundred. The purpose of the hunting, according to the State Fish and Game Commission, is to keep the elk from multiplying past the carrying capacity of their present range. However, the official count in 1967, including calves, was only 246, so no hunt was allowed that year.

Conservationists feel that such a rare animal should not be held down to so small a number, but should, instead, be given range preference. So the Committee for the Preservation of the Tule Elk, supported by about sixty conservation organizations and more than two thousand individuals, waged a crusade to have the south half of the Owens Valley set aside as a preserve for the elk. The area is owned by the City of Los Angeles but is leased to cattlemen, and they, naturally, do not look with favor on this plan. The conservationists, on the other hand, believe that there is a much greater scarcity of tule elk than of beef cattle.

The crusade apparently succeeded when the Los Angeles City Council, by unanimous vote, authorized "that portion of Owens Valley land lying between Tinemaha and Owens Lake, be set aside as a wildlife refuge." But actual protection of the elk in the area seems to be slow in coming.

However, the people of California take pride in the fact that this rare animal, along with the California condor, is found only in their state and nowhere else in the world. So the public will surely demand that this sanctuary be maintained to preserve the tule elk and other wildlife in the area.

THE KAIBAB SQUIRREL

The Kaibab squirrel is considered the most beautiful squirrel in America. His white, plume-like tail contrasts sharply with his

This Kaibab squirrel is enjoying a meal of nuts in Grand Canyon National Park, Arizona.

dark-gray sides and black breast. A broad chestnut stripe runs down his back from his neck to the base of his tail, and there are tufts of black hair, an inch or more long, on his pointed ears. He loses these tufts in June, but they grow back in the fall. Because of them, he is called a "tassel-eared" squirrel.

We have only two tassel-eared species—the Kaibab squirrel and the Abert squirrel. Scientists believe that these two species evolved from a common ancestor far back in the Ice Age. When the Grand Canyon was formed, part of the tassel-ears stayed on one side of it and part on the other. Thus divided, these two groups, over a period of many thousands of years, developed different characteristics. Instead of black underparts and a white tail, the Abert squirrel has a white breast and a gray tail, white underneath. The two species are about the same size—twenty to twenty-two inches long from the tip of the nose to the tip of the tail, and one and a half to two pounds in weight.

Both squirrels like the same kind of habitat—yellow pines at an altitude of 6000 to 8500 feet. Their living habits are similar, and they eat very much the same kinds of food—mushrooms and other fungi, acorns, conifer seeds, and, most important, the cambium layer under the outer bark of small pine branches. The squirrel gets to this inner layer by cutting off short lengths of the branch and stripping off the outer bark.

When the tassel-ear is disturbed in his search for food along the floor of the forest, he moves like a flash to the nearest tree. Instead of hiding, however, he often sits on a branch in plain sight, his tail twitching in anger, and hurls noisy insults at who-ever interrupted his dinner. This delights the tourist who, per-haps, has lingered in the forest with the hope of catching a glimpse of this little creature. But it also makes the squirrel a tempting target for a hunter with an itching trigger finger, who would like to add one more small pelt to those in his game bag.

The Abert squirrel lives on the South Rim of the Grand Can-yon, and is also found in New Mexico and Colorado; but the Kaibab squirrel is limited to a narrow belt of pine forest on the North Rim of the Canyon. This land "island" on which he lives —about eight hundred square miles—has the Grand Canyon on the south and deserts on the other three sides. There are probably about one thousand Kaibab squirrels, including about one hun-dred in Grand Canyon National Park. No one is very sure of the exact number, however, since it is difficult to take an accurate squirrel census.

Although the Kaibab squirrel is extremely rare, the Arizona Game and Fish Commission ordered an open hunting season on it for the fall of 1964, to be held at the same time as the one on wild turkeys. There is an open season on the not-so-rare Abert squirrel; so, reasoned the Commission, why not have one on the Kaibab squirrel as well? The announcement met with such an uproar of protest from all over the nation, however, that the Commission hurriedly rescinded the order for an open season on both the squirrels and the turkeys.

Other threats to the Kaibab squirrel are disease, and death on the highway. A number of squirrels are killed annually by cars, a danger that could be reduced or eliminated entirely if motorists could be persuaded to drive carefully and watch out for wildlife on the highway.

Chapter 6

THE ALLIGATOR

He lay quietly on the bank of the little canal and watched us —a crowd of us—across the narrow strip of water. His big, darkly gleaming eyes were set well back on his long, narrow head, and they made two little hills that stood up higher than the rest of his head. Now and then his eyelids would blink slowly shut, then open again.

The long jaws were closed, and he lay with his throat flat against the ground. But as we watched, he lifted his head a little, coming up on his two front feet, and we could see the creamy leatherish covering of plates on his throat and breast. The jaws opened slightly, to show wicked-looking teeth, and the crowd sent up a quick gasp at the threatening, self-assured look of him.

He looked us over, regal, not afraid of anything. Then he dropped his head again, and his whole length—ten or twelve feet or more—seemed to relax and sink flatter against the ground.

We were watching one of the biggest alligators in Everglades National Park, in southern Florida. The little canal is part of Taylor Slough, and we were standing on the path leading to the boardwalk called "Anhinga Trail." We had seen several other alligators from the boardwalk, and there were two others here— but they were all smaller. This was the big one. Like a big cat in the jungle, like an eagle in the air, like a grizzly bear in the mountains, he was King.

If a slough is drained, alligators, turtles, and many other animals are left to die.

It was almost dark, and time for us to go; but we had not seen nearly enough of Anhinga Trail to satisfy us. So we went back to the Trail first thing in the morning. When we walked up the path along the canal, we saw a horrifying sight.

The King was dead. The big alligator lay on his back in the water. Someone, during the night, had shot him. Park rangers were pulling him out of the water, and they found a hole where a bullet had plowed into the back of his head, through his brain, and out through his throat.

No one knew who had shot him. The rangers thought the killer might be a poacher, come to strip off the alligator's skin and sell it. If so, the poacher had probably been frightened away by a ranger on night patrol, before he could get the valuable skin.

Some people fear that the 'gator's "built-in smile" is misleading. Teeth, eyes, nose, and heavily armored body and legs combine to help this animal stalk and catch his prey.

Or perhaps this was vandalism. Although guns are not allowed in the Park, this could be the result of a forbidden gun in the hands of someone who could not resist shooting at anything alive, regardless of what or where.

But it was sad indeed to see this big animal lifeless, unmoving and unknowing, when just last night he had been so powerful, so unafraid.

Man is, actually, almost the only enemy that an adult alligator needs to fear. In fact, an alligator three to four feet long—two to three years old—has almost no enemies in the animal world except other alligators, and he is still not an adult. It will be two or three years more before he reaches a mature size of five to six feet. From then on, he continues to grow, but at a slower rate.

An alligator comes well equipped to defend himself. His back is layered with hide-covered bony plates so thick and tough that they are an almost impenetrable armor. On his sides and belly the scales, or plates, are thinner and more flexible, but even there it is hard for an enemy to puncture them. An alligator is not often attacked by some other animal; if he is, the animal is usually another alligator.

But there is no lying still on the part of the 'gator if a panther or a bear tries to get at that sweet, juicy meat of his underside. True, if an attack is made on land, the 'gator may be at a disadvantage, because his rather short and weak legs do not help him much. But he can slap that long tail of his toward his jaws with amazing power. He can roll over like a flash, dragging his enemy with him and beating it to death. And once those big jaws clamp down on something, that something is probably a goner. He can close his jaws with such force that no man could pry them apart; and he has been known to close them down so hard on a steel bar that his teeth were forced backward through the top of his jaw.

Why, then, have men been able to capture so many big alligators alive, for zoos and animal shows? There is a very strange fact about the 'gator's jaws. In spite of all that power, the big muscles at the side of the 'gator's neck can be brought into play only when the jaws are closing. The opening action is so weak that once the jaws are closed, a man can put his hands around the 'gator's nose and hold them closed.

Even so, few men (unless they have a gun) and almost no wild animal can match an alligator once he is in the water. He moves with almost unbelievable swiftness, both at the surface of the water and beneath it. He tucks his legs close in against his body, and his powerful tail sweeps gracefully from side to side to send him shooting along, faster than any land animal can swim. He comes neatly alongside, swings his head sidewise, jaws open, in a lightning thrust, and grabs whatever it is he is chasing for his dinner.

Often he lies in wait for his prey, sometimes on the bank of a stream or lake, sometimes floating quietly under the surface of the water, with just the knobs of his eyes and his lumpy nose rising above it. As he lies there, fish move into the water around him. Slowly he sinks beneath the surface. Then a splash of stampeded fish will shatter the water as he strikes, and he comes up with a big garfish in his mouth.

His eyesight is unusually good, and so is his hearing, through ears that lie just back of his eyes. The ears are covered with flaps of thick skin that he closes when he goes under water. His nose, too, is an underwater nose, with flaps that close the nostrils when he is beneath the surface. His eyes are like a cat's, with a pupil that narrows to a slit in bright light, and opens wide when the light is poor. Reflecting light at night, the "eyeshine" is red; then all you can see of the alligator is two bright red "lights."

Alligators eat almost any animals they can catch—fish, turtles, frogs, snails, muskrats, ducks and other water birds, even, sometimes, their own young. They eat snakes, poisonous and nonpoisonous, and do not seem to be bothered if the snake succeeds

Here looking like an old log, the alligator can sink still deeper into the water, until only his high-set eyes and the tip of his nose show above it.

in biting them "on the way down." Garfish are a favorite food, and since garfish eat a great many bass and other game fish, fishermen like to see alligators in their lakes and streams. They maintain that wherever there are alligators there is good fishing.

Two things, besides food and air, that alligators must have are warmth and water. If a 'gator gets too cold, he becomes numb and helpless; if he gets too dry, he dies.

Alligators in Louisiana and Georgia meet the winter cold by building a winter den. Somewhere along the bank of a bayou or river or lake, the alligator "digs in." He goes under water and digs into the bank with his feet. His front feet have five toes, his hind feet four; and the first three toes of each foot have sharp claws—fine tools for loosening the earth. He may use his teeth to cut through tough roots, and his nose to dig into the earth.

He pushes the loose earth backward as far as he can while he works. Then he sweeps that heavy tail back and forth, back and forth, until the mud is swept away. He digs deeper into the bank, and again sweeps the mud away with his tail. Again and again, he digs and sweeps, digs and sweeps, until he has tunneled far back under the bank.

The water follows him into his tunnel, and if this is tidewater and the tide is rising, it may completely fill the tunnel, closing over his head. So he may widen out a little room at the end of the tunnel, a bit higher than the rest of it, where there will always be an air space between the water and the ceiling. Or he may make, here and there, small holes up to the surface of the ground. When water comes into his tunnel, he puts his nose up against one of these holes to get the little air he needs.

Winter after winter, the same alligator may come back to a den. He may enlarge it a little each year. He may make additional tunnels branching off from it. He may have more than one entrance.

He spends the cold, stormy days in his den, moving little, breathing little, eating nothing. On sunny days, he may climb out on the bank above his den and sun himself for a while; but still he does not eat, from early in October to late in March.

Farther south, in central and southern Florida, alligators are much more active during the winter. They dig shallow dens under the banks of the rivers, or perhaps hollow out a deeper spot in the bottom of a pond, and they go into these dens during the coldest spells of weather. They do not feed in these cold times, either. But through warm, sunny weeks, even in winter, they are active, and feed along the banks of rivers and in swamps and sloughs.

In times of drought, alligators dig holes deep into the muddy bottom of a pond or a marsh that is drying up. Water drains into the hole, or it may be deep enough to reach the water table. So a little reservoir is formed where the alligator can live until the rains come again. Other kinds of water animals can live in the reservoir too—insects, minnows and other fish, frogs, whatever has lived in the pond. Some of these will be eaten by the alligator, but many escape him. Later, when water comes again, these small forms spread out and start the restocking of their wetlands; they are a vital link in the food chain that supports all wildlife. Land animals, too, can come to the 'gator holes for a saving drink of water. So the alligators help in the survival of many kinds of wildlife.

Spring is the mating time for alligators, and then it is we hear the male's deep, booming roar, a bellow that can be heard for miles. If a second male comes into the first one's territory, the two will fight until one is driven off. After the mating period, the male goes his way, leaving the female to build a nest, lay her eggs, and protect her young—something that most reptile mothers do not do. She will protect her young even from the male, driving him away if he does not go of his own accord. If he should be around when the young hatch, he might eat them.

The mother alligator builds her nest by piling up a big stack of plants, roots, sticks, and mud that she has torn up from the water. She chooses a dry spot on land for her nest, usually quite near the water where her den is; or, if she is in the middle of a marsh, she may choose a clump of reeds and build the stack on this raised hummock. She carries the building materials in her mouth, and flattens and packs them into the nest mound by sliding back and forth across it.

When the mound is high enough to suit her, she pushes the top out and rounds out a hollow by sweeping her tail back and forth across it. She lays all her eggs in this hollow and all of them at one time. If she is nesting for the first time, she may lay no more than thirty eggs. If she is a large alligator, she may lay as many as seventy-five or eighty.

She covers the eggs with a muddy mixture of torn-up leaves and stems of plants, and packs them down firmly. As the plant mixture decays, it produces heat, and so, insulated by the mud, the eggs stay warm night and day.

An alligator nest, broken open, reveals a clutch of long, oval eggs. Decaying vegetation keeps them warm.

Alligator eggs are a favorite food of many animals—raccoons, wild pigs, opossums, bears, and many others. They find it easy to tear open the top of the nest and reach the fine-flavored eggs. But the mother alligator stays near the nest to guard it, and rushes, hissing loudly, mouth wide open, at any enemy that comes near.

If the marauder persists in disturbing the nest, she will attack and fight until he is dead or driven off.

In about two months the little alligators are ready to hatch. Each one breaks its way out of the tough eggshell with a small, pointed pick on its nose. They grunt as they hatch, making a shrill "Umph, umph, umph!" When their mother hears them grunting, she opens the top of the nest, and they can get out of it. She goes to the water and they follow her, running quickly into it, and she takes them to her den. There she protects them until they are large enough to look after themselves. They stay with her all summer and winter and into the next spring.

WHY IS THE ALLIGATOR DISAPPEARING?

Here are thirty-five to eighty little alligators, or an average of about sixty, produced in a single brood by a pair of mature adults. They are quick and agile in the water the minute they reach it.

This newly-hatched baby alligator can run on land, and swim like a fish. But she will be five or six years old before she will be large enough to lay eggs.

They can catch fish and other food with the greatest of ease. Their mother stands by to protect them from enemies. Why, then, are alligators on the list of animals that we may lose?

There are some interesting answers to that question. One is that, protected though he may be, the little alligator is the natural prey of many larger animals. Until he is somewhere around three feet long, he is regularly killed and eaten by raccoons, bobcats, bears, cougars, snapping turtles, and any other predatory animal that may come across him—including, sometimes, larger alligators. So out of a large brood of baby alligators, only a few may survive to become mature.

Another answer is that a female alligator must grow to be five or six years old before she lays eggs. So ten or twelve years go by from the time a female hatches until her daughter is laying eggs. This means that not nearly as many little alligators are produced every year as that brood of sixty or more might lead us to guess.

Still, these are natural hazards that have existed through the centuries, and the few alligators that may survive from each brood have been enough to bring this big reptile down to our time in large numbers. He, along with other members of the crocodile family, is the closest living relative of the dinosaurs. He developed on the earth some two hundred million years ago, and he walked it all through the time of the dinosaurs, even though some of them were so big and fierce that they could swallow him in two gulps.

Clearly, his ability to fit into his natural environment is remarkable—he can fend for himself, secure a variety of food, make himself a place of safety in cold weather, and produce and protect the young that will carry on his species. He has been doing all these things for thousands and thousands of years.

But modern times have brought a change—man as the alligator's enemy. Some of the things man does may entirely wipe out this big reptile from America's wild living things.

From an estimated three million wild alligators in the southern states a hundred years ago, we have only a few thousand today —no one knows just how many. One authority estimates that we have only ten percent of those living ten years ago. What has happened to bring about this sudden decrease in numbers?

One thing that has happened is that man is draining many of the wetlands where alligators live. In Florida, for example, only half of the original Everglades will still support wildlife. Highways, airports, pipelines, power lines, and drainage for water control are taking more wetlands every year.

Everglades National Park is almost the last large natural stronghold of the alligators. But since water control projects north of the Park have reduced its water supplies, the 'gators have suffered, even here. In 1965 Taylor Slough went completely dry, its mud bottom caked by the sun and marked by the last of the alligators as they crawled along it, seeking water. The 'gator holes were dry too, and dig as they would, the alligators could not get down far enough to reach water. When the Park rangers could, they caught the alligators and moved them to some luckier spot that still had a little water. And holes were dynamited at places where the water table could be reached, and a little water came to the surface in these "man-made 'gator holes."

Even when the alligator manages to find himself a suitable home, he is often not left to enjoy it for long. In every state where alligators live in the wild, except Texas, there are laws against killing him. Yet if he comes into a lake or marsh near where people live, they may feel that he threatens them and their families, and they can ask police officers to get rid of him. Sometimes he is trapped and moved to a wildlife refuge, but often, in these cases, he is killed. Several alligators in a lake in St. Petersburg, Florida, were killed by police in 1967 because people living near the lake insisted that they were a menace to human life.

Yet, in spite of his power, the alligator is quite a timid animal with human beings. He may become bold enough to attack, if he is often fed by people. But he seldom attacks a person unless he is being molested. He will fight a ranger or game warden who is trying to move him from one place to another, but he is very unlikely to attack someone who is not bothering him.

Men kill a great many alligators for another reason, even though it is against the law. The alligator's hide is very valuable. The tan or creamy covering of his underside makes a beautiful leather, and is manufactured into shoes, purses, belts, and other articles. So poachers make a business of killing alligators and selling their hides, getting as much as eight dollars a foot for them. For two men working in a boat, it takes only a few minutes to shoot an alligator, strip off the beautiful underside skin, and move on to a new location. It is hard to catch them at it, because they work at night, and they work quickly and quietly.

In a long dry spell, such as often comes to the south in the spring and early summer, many of the ponds and sloughs dry up. So the alligators are forced to leave them and search for water somewhere else, often in open canals or other places where they have no cover. This means that they congregate in unprotected places, and so are "sitting ducks" for poachers.

Many of today's alligators live in sanctuaries where wildlife is protected, such as Everglades National Park, and Okeefenokee Swamp National Wildlife Refuge in Georgia. There are many smaller sanctuaries and parks where a few alligators live. But in all of them the big reptiles can be victims of poachers who will take the risk of being arrested to get the valuable hides.

Hunting alligators has long been a profitable occupation on the Gulf Coast; one authority estimates that, between 1800 and 1900, a million 'gators a year were harvested for their skins. It is not very likely that this hunting will be stopped until either the alligator or the market disappears. Such occurrences as the shooting of the alligator in Everglades National Park, while not common, still demonstrate how easy it is to kill an alligator.

So those who would save the alligator from extinction are trying today to do away with the market for skins. Legislators are working on a law against shipping or receiving skins from states that protect alligators. In the meantime, the public is being asked to boycott alligator products—to buy no purse or shoes or other object made of alligator skin. If manufacturers stop buying alligator skins, poachers will stop killing alligators.

Then, perhaps, ten years from now, there will still be alligators in the wild, and we will not need to fear that at any minute someone may shoot that big King we saw last night.

Chapter 7

LIVING GOLD

Living gold! That is what much of our wildlife has been, literally, to many people; and some of it still is, today. Our commercial fisheries, for instance, are doing a multimillion-dollar business, and our fur-bearing animals—seals, beavers, mink, and others—are still supplying the world with millions of dollars' worth of furs.

But all that is a mere pittance to the living gold our wildlife would be if it hadn't been so ruthlessly slaughtered. When billions of passenger pigeons darkened the skies and millions of buffalo roamed the plains, it didn't seem possible that there could ever be a shortage. But in twenty short years, beginning with 1865, professional hunters reduced an estimated sixty million buffalo to less than five hundred; in a few more years, these were cut to less than one hundred.

Finally people woke up to the fact that there would soon be no buffalo at all, and our national government took steps to protect those that were left. Now there are about five thousand in the United States, most of them in state and national parks and wildlife refuges. And there are about fifteen thousand wood buffalo, a subspecies slightly larger and darker than our plains buffalo, in Canada.

The wholesale slaughter of American egrets for their "courting plumage," or aigrettes, put them on the endangered list until laws were passed to protect them. The courting plumage appears only during the courting and nesting season; death of the parents at that season leaves the young birds to starve.

91

Almost lost, the big, interesting American buffalo, or bison, lives today only in protected areas.

The story of the passenger pigeon is even more heartbreaking. These pigeons, called "the most impressive species of bird that man has ever known," were once present in the eastern half of the United States in such vast numbers that people thought the supply could never be exhausted. They searched for food and migrated in such large flocks that they blotted out the sun for several hours at a time, and the beat of their wings sounded as if a tornado was passing. John James Audubon estimated a billion birds or more in one such flock.

It was probably this habit of gathering in such large flocks that brought about the pigeons' extinction, because they were an easy prey for market hunters, deadliest of all professional hunters. They killed them with guns and clubs and lured them, with live decoys, into huge nets. The late William T. Hornaday, one of the first scientists to write about our endangered wildlife, told about one town in Michigan that shipped, in 1869, three carloads of dead pigeons to market every day for forty days, a total of 11,880,000 birds.

Finally some of the states began to pass laws to protect the pigeon, but it was "too little and too late." The last known pair were killed in 1898, and the last lone survivor died in a Cincinnati zoo in 1914. Even then, people could not believe that the passenger pigeon had really vanished from the earth. Large cash awards, totaling about five thousand dollars, were offered for the discovery of one nesting pair; but the awards were never claimed.

Market hunters very nearly exterminated other species, too, including the "plume birds" of the South. These are the white American egret and the snowy egret, whose courting plumes made the handsome aigrettes that women once wore on their hats; and the roseate spoonbill, whose lovely pink and rose feathers were likewise in demand as fashion ornaments. When laws were passed against such use of their plumes, the egrets quickly increased until they are again common in the southeast. The roseate spoonbill is still somewhat rare, however, depending upon the success of its rookeries in Everglades National Park.

Market hunters also threatened many of our shore birds and even some of the songbirds. Gradually, however, state and federal legislation has been passed to protect songbirds and migratory birds, and today most species of birds are protected to some extent, at least.

The laws did not come in time to save the Carolina parakeet, the only wild parrot that lived in North America's temperate zone. Market hunters killed this handsome bird for its green and yellow and orange feathers, in demand for women's hats; and farmers killed it because it ate their grain and fruit. So it was soon exterminated.

Two more wildlife species played an important part in the exploration and settlement of Canada and the United States and were nearly exterminated in the process—the beaver and the trumpeter swan.

THE BEAVER

When the white man came to North America and began to explore what is now the United States and Canada, millions of beavers lived in the streams and lakes. This animal, largest rodent in North America, has two layers of fur, a long, coarse, outer fur over a thick, soft, inner layer. The two layers keep the beaver warm and comfortable, either on land or in the water. When the long fur is plucked away from a beaver skin, the inner fur can be made into a beautiful, warm coat; so the fur is quite valuable.

In the eighteenth and nineteenth centuries, beaver hats as well as coats became very fashionable in Europe. Trappers and fur traders pushed deep into the wilderness in search of the precious skins. Fur companies, like the Hudson Bay Company, were founded, and trading posts sprang up along the principal waterways, on spots where some of our largest cities now stand. The Indians and white trappers bartered their beaver pelts to the fur traders for food and clothing and guns and whatever else they wanted or needed. Hundreds of thousands of furs, largely beaver pelts, were shipped to Europe every year, and vast fortunes were made.

Trapping of beavers continued into the twentieth century, until they almost became extinct. When laws were passed to protect them, however, they made a rapid comeback and are no longer on the "threatened" list. But they will never again be as plentiful as they were in the early days of our country.

THE TRUMPETER SWAN

The trumpeter swans were also victims of early-day trade with Europe, when the Hudson Bay Company and other fur-trading companies each year sent thousands of swan skins to European markets. The skins were greatly prized for down and for feathers, used for decoration and for writing quills. Indians killed many of the birds for food as well as for barter with the fur traders. When white settlers spread westward, they added to the slaughter of the swans.

Trumpeter swans once ranged throughout much of North America. In early spring they were a spectacular sight as they moved in great flocks to their nesting grounds in Alaska and Arctic Canada; they nested as far south as Iowa and northern

These baby trumpeters, with five others hatched in the Philadelphia zoo, were the first in more than one hundred years to be produced in captivity in the United States. They were hatched, and photographed, in a city park in Great Bend, Kansas.

A pair of trumpeter swans fly over Red Rock Lakes National Refuge in Montana. This sight has become possible with the snatching of the trumpeters from the very edge of extinction.

Missouri, and as far east as Indiana. In the fall they returned to their wintering grounds along the central Atlantic and Gulf coasts, in the Ohio and Mississippi valleys, and along the lower Columbia River on the west coast. But at the end of the nineteenth century, the great flocks were seen no more, and scientists were predicting the extinction of this beautiful bird, largest of all North American waterfowl.

By 1934 only seventy-three wild trumpeters could be found in the United States; most of these were in the Red Rock Lakes area in southwestern Montana, and in nearby Yellowstone National Park. State and national laws had been passed to protect the swans, and conservationists were fighting to save the big birds, but illegal killing was still going on, and the situation looked almost hopeless. Then the United States Biological Survey, which later became the United States Fish and Wildlife Service, succeeded in getting a forty-thousand-acre national wildlife refuge established in the Red Rock Lakes area. The story of how the management of this refuge, with the help of the National Park Service and other agencies and organizations, saved the trumpeters and increased their numbers to nearly seven hundred by 1964 is one of the most encouraging in the history of conservation.

The Red Rock Lakes National Wildlife Refuge lies in the east end of Montana's Centennial Valley, about fifty miles west of Yellowstone National Park. This valley, which has an altitude of sixty-six hundred feet, is a broad trough between two high mountain ranges, whose towering peaks are snowcapped the year round. The runoff from the snow, as well as numerous springs and streams in the valley, provide a steady supply of water to the lakes and marshes. The area is an ideal habitat for the trumpeter swans and was probably used by them long before men came to the North American continent.

The trumpeter swan is sometimes mistaken for the whistling swan, which is much more numerous; but the trumpeter is larger, with a wingspread of six feet or more. And its deep, hornlike call is quite different from the high-pitched "whistle" of the whistling swan. The adults have white plumage and black bills and feet. The young birds, called "cygnets," are gray. The adult male is known as a "cob," and the female as a "pen." Swans mate for life, but if one of the pair dies, the other one may take another mate.

In the Red Rock Lakes Refuge, the swans usually nest on the tops of muskrat houses. They nest in late April or early May, and the female lays from five to nine eggs. It takes about five weeks for the eggs to hatch, and the cygnets take to the water almost immediately. They swim with their parents and feed on water plants, but they are not able to fly until the following autumn. The adult trumpeters molt their flight feathers during the summer, and for a month or so, they, too, are unable to fly.

Because of hot-water springs on the Refuge, some of the lakes and springs do not freeze over in the winter, and most of the swans do not migrate, except for short trips across the range to the North Fork of the Snake River, in Idaho. The fact that these

trumpeters do not make the long, dangerous trip to distant wintering grounds has helped to reduce illegal shooting and other
threats to the safety of the big birds. The Refuge management
gives the swans supplementary feedings during the winter months,
and protects their nesting sites from harmful disturbance by people during the summer nesting season.

Like whooping cranes, each pair of trumpeters requires a large
territory in which to nest. When the swan population became so
large that there was no longer room for all of them to nest on the
Refuge, the management worked out a plan to transplant some
of them to other areas. Breeding pairs and cygnets were sent to
the National Elk Refuge in Wyoming, the Malheur National
Wildlife Refuge in Oregon, Ruby Lake National Wildlife Refuge in Nevada, and the Lacreek National Wildlife Refuge in
South Dakota. The swans have nested successfully in all these
areas. The rejoicing was great when the first cygnets were hatched
at Lacreek in 1963, because these were the first trumpeter swans
to hatch east of the United States Rockies in eighty years.

The Bureau of Sport Fisheries and Wildlife also loans trumpeter
swans to zoos throughout the country so that people can see these
beautiful birds. There are now about one thousand wild trumpeters in the United States, including about two hundred in
Alaska, and there are probably eight hundred in Canada. So the
trumpeter swans have been taken off the threatened list, although
they will never again migrate in large flocks along the flyways.

LIVING GOLD TWICE OVER

The manatee, rare water mammal also called "sea cow," could
once be found in fairly large numbers along the coastal waters
and lagoons from southern Texas to Florida, and, in the warmer
months, as far north as North Carolina. But so many were killed
for oil and meat—its flesh is quite similar to beef—that it is now
threatened with extinction. People still shoot at it, although it has

The manatee is a water mammal and must come to the surface of the water to breathe.

been protected by law in Florida since 1907.

Many Florida manatees today live in Everglades National Park, and others may be found around the Florida Keys, in the Miami area, and as far north as the St. Johns River at Jacksonville. However, the manatee is strictly an animal of the tropics and subtropics, and many of them have died when Florida's temperature took a sudden drop.

The manatee lays no claim to beauty. It has a small, grotesque head, front flippers but no hind limbs, and a long body ending in a flat, rounded tail. It is from seven to fifteen feet long and may weigh from five hundred to two thousand pounds. The baby manatee is about thirty inches long at birth; it is born in the water, and so must learn quickly to swim and come to the surface of the water for air.

Often compared to whale and porpoise, the manatee is not related to either one. Its only close relatives are other subspecies of manatee, found in the West Indies and along the east coast of Central and South America; and the dugongs of Australia and Africa. The Steller sea cow, a huge northern species that grew to thirty feet long, once lived along the coast of Bering Island. But Russian sailors found its meat to be especially tasty, and, just twenty-seven years after it was discovered, they had killed every one. By 1769 the Steller sea cow was extinct.

So the manatee was once "living gold" to the Indians and whalers. Now, if it is saved from extinction, it may be living gold in quite a different way. Large sums of money are spent every year to keep southern rivers and canals from being clogged by water hyacinths and other water weeds—the favorite food of manatees. One manatee will eat a hundred pounds of such vegetation in a day.

Experiments were financed by the Central and Southern Flood Control District and carried out under the direction of Dr. Peter Sguros of Florida Atlantic University, to find out whether manatees could be used in Florida as a practical control for water weeds. Florida news mediums gave considerable space to these experiments when it was discovered that five sea cows could open a half mile of weed-clogged canal in about three weeks. In another month's time, they cleaned out all vegetation, even from the mud on the bottom.

Further studies were made to learn more about the manatee and its living habits, in an effort to save it from extinction. However, before the studies could be completed, all but one of the manatees in the experiments died; and the project ran out of money. Most of the sea cows probably died as a result of a temperature drop; but one was the victim of vandals, who shot nearly a hundred bullets into it.

Before the manatees can truly become "living gold," some way must be devised to protect them from spells of cold weather and from men with guns. And their numbers will have to be considerably increased. As matters stand today, no one knows how many are alive.

OTHER RICHES FROM THE SEA

Man has long been able to take great wealth from the sea. Among the sea animals that have been most valuable to him are the whales and the seals.

The Alaska, or northern, fur seal, world-wide supplier of seal-skin furs, is so far from being endangered that a "harvest" of these animals can be taken each year. Once there were five million or more in Pacific Ocean waters ranging along the entire Pacific Coast. They returned each year to breeding grounds on the tiny Pribilof Islands in the Bering Sea, southwest of Alaska— and here, as well as in the open sea, they were heedlessly slaughtered. But some years after the United States bought Alaska and the Pribilofs, an international treaty stopped unrestricted killing. Today a limited annual "harvest" of large male seals has allowed the herd to increase again to around two million adults, and the revenue from this "renewable resource" has paid the purchase price of Alaska several times over.

The Guadalupe fur seal has not fared as well. Once it was fairly common along the coast of southern California and Baja California, in Mexico. Today only a few hundred still live around Guadalupe Island, Mexico; once thought to be extinct, they are among the rarest of North American mammals. They are protected by the laws of Mexico and California, and are thought to be increasing.

The monk seals, too, are in trouble. The Caribbean monk seal, once common offshore from Caribbean countries and the Florida Keys, met the same kind of slaughter as the northern seals. It has not been seen for more than fifteen years and may be extinct. The Hawaiian monk seal, of which there are about fifteen hundred, is protected in the Hawaiian Islands National Wildlife Refuge.

Whales are valuable commercially for an especially fine grade of oil and for the resilient, elastic whalebone or "baleen." To the Eskimo they supply many life needs—oil, meat, and the fat that becomes blubber. Commercial whaling—the catching and killing of whales from special ships built for that purpose—has long been practised. But the numbers of whales are diminishing in all the

Baby green turtles go scooting across the sand to the sea, always choosing the right direction to find it.

world's oceans—the big kinds of whales that are profitable to catch.

Some of the endangered species have been given international protection and may again be on the increase. One of these is the gray whale, a big fellow forty-five feet long, that lives in the Pacific from Alaska to Baja California. Gray whales are often seen from the Pacific mainland, migrating in great numbers in the fall to their southern breeding grounds, and back to the North in the spring. There may be about eight thousand of them in existence.

Largest animal ever to live on the earth is the blue whale. This giant of them all may measure one hundred feet long and weigh one hundred and fifty tons. Imagine its baby at birth—twenty-five feet long! Or its heart, weighing half a ton, or its tongue, over four tons! The blue whale, too, may be in trouble. In the north Atlantic there may be only a few hundred of them, and probably less than fifteen hundred in the north Pacific.

The Atlantic right whale and the Pacific right whale, so valuable that these were once said to be "the *right* whales to catch," are both reduced to probably only a few hundred each, one kind along the Atlantic coast, the other along the Pacific. The humpback whale also lives off both coasts and may exceed five thousand; and the bowhead whale, perhaps one thousand of him, lives in northern oceans, coming as far south as the Pribilof Islands and the Gulf of Mexico. All of these are big whales, measuring from forty to seventy feet; all are valuable; and all are more or less protected by international treaty from indiscriminate whaling.

OPERATION GREEN TURTLE

Green turtles, too, come from the sea, and they are sometimes called the most valuable of all reptiles. They live most of their lives in the open sea, where they eat turtle grass growing on the sea bottom. They have lungs and so must come to the surface

A green turtle comes ashore at Turtle Bogue to lay her eggs.

of the water every few minutes to breathe. They mate offshore, in the water. But the female turtle leaves the water and comes up on a sandy beach to lay her eggs. Then she is vulnerable. Then she can be, and is, easily caught and carried off to the marketplace.

Weighing between two hundred fifty and five hundred pounds, she uses her flippers to drag herself through the sand, leaving a wide, deeply marked track. She goes well back from the water, to bushes or to the foot of a dune. There, with her front flippers, she digs out a big hollow to lie in. With her back flippers she digs a hole at the bottom of the hollow to hold the eggs. In it she lays twenty or more round, white eggs about the size of golf balls. She carefully fills the hole and the hollow with sand, and then she returns to the water.

On a Caribbean beach, she may lay six or seven times in a season, from June to October, depositing a total of perhaps two hundred eggs. As she leaves the water, she is always wary and is easily startled and frightened back into it. But once she is nest-building and laying, she pays no attention to anything going on around her.

In about sixty days the young turtles hatch from the eggs. They claw their way up through the sand in the nest. Then they head for the water, knowing at once and unerringly where it is. No one knows just where they go, once in the water, or what they eat. But since young turtles raised in captivity thrive on chopped fish, it is believed they live on the great numbers of tiny animals that are all around them in the water. Later, as older turtles, they have favorite feeding grounds where the turtle grass grows, in the Gulf of Mexico off Florida and Mexico, in the Caribbean Sea off Central America, in the Atlantic Ocean off South America and Africa, in the Pacific and Indian oceans.

Wherever they go to feed and spend most of their lives, it is believed that when they nest, they always come back to the same beach where they were hatched. A female does not come every year; she may miss two or three years between layings. But it has been fairly well proved that when she is ready to lay, she returns to the beach where she nested before.

Why are green turtles valuable? The cartilage between the turtle's body and its shell is used to make the world-famous green-turtle soup. The flesh is used as turtle steak; at one time it was, to peoples living near the sea, as important as beef or the meat of other animals. The skin of the neck and front flippers is increasingly in demand for leather. All of these bring good prices in the world's markets.

So there has been, and is, such a profitable traffic in these big, easily caught turtles that their abundance has been greatly decreased. Especially in the Gulf of Mexico and in the Caribbean, where once there were many nesting beaches, there is now only one—Tortuguero Beach, or Turtle Bogue, a twenty-two-mile-long beach in Costa Rica. A few individuals or small colonies may nest in other widely scattered areas. (The best place in the United States to see a green turtle is in one of the big aquariums; any of them probably has one or two or more green turtles in its tanks.)

In the United States and in Costa Rica and a few other localities, a nesting green turtle and her eggs and nest are protected by law. But there are many poachers on the nesting beaches, who watch for the females to come to the beach and take them immediately, even before they can lay their eggs. So these illegal hunters destroy adult turtles and the new generation as well.

To find out about green turtles and try to stop their dwindling, several organizations were formed in Caribbean countries and in the United States. Dr. Archie Carr, zoologist from the University of Florida, was placed in charge of the work—of "Operation Green Turtle." He and other scientists set up an experimental hatchery at Turtle Bogue, in which eggs are gathered from the beach and hatched. The young turtles are kept there in tanks for about a year, protected from the many enemies in the sea that prey on them when they are very small.

Then they are flown by the United States Navy to other beaches and released—beaches in Florida and Texas, Mexico and Central America, islands in the Caribbean, and South America. In ten years, one hundred thousand little turtles have been released. It is hoped that they will return to the "adopted" beaches to nest, and so will re-establish some of the big nesting colonies that once existed.

The experimenters can track adult turtles by attaching tiny transistor radios to their shells. They have learned that turtles tagged off South America swam fourteen hundred miles to Ascension Island, a tiny island in the middle of the Atlantic Ocean, to lay their eggs. How did they find the way? No one knows, but Operation Green Turtle is trying to find out.

But no satisfactory tag for the baby turtles has been developed. An attached tag may fall off; a marker of any kind is probably absorbed as the turtle grows from a few ounces to several hundred pounds.

Sea otters sun themselves on the rocky coast of Amchitka Island, in the

So, when two female green turtles came in 1966 to a beach on Hutchinson Island, off Florida's east coast, and laid their eggs, and again two came in 1967, there was no way to be sure that they were some of Florida's "adopted" turtles. But hopes are high that they were—that the plan is working, and that this is the beginning of new colonies of nesting green turtles.

A HAPPY ENDING

Of all the storied animals that America is heir to, the sea otter, perhaps, is in the lead. It is one of the most valuable and one of the most appealing of all our animals.

Sea otters live along the Pacific Coast, in the surf and quiet ocean near the mainland or around islands. The northern or Alaskan subspecies lives in the Aleutians and islands off the Alaska coast; the southern, or California, sea otter lives along the California coast from Monterey Bay to Moro Bay.

Somewhat like our river otters, the sea otter is much larger; he is about four and a half feet long and may weigh up to eighty-five pounds. He is a mammal and has a coat of fur—fine, soft, thick fur that protects him from the water. His front feet are

Aleutians. A "pup" is almost hidden by the big adult on the right.

paws, his hind feet flippers. With them he can send himself shooting through the water, twisting, turning, treading water, and
playing with other sea otters. His body is slim and streamlined
and very strong. He has a round head and such a sheaf of grayish whiskers that he is sometimes called "old man of the sea."
Those who have seen his comic face and watched his antics in
the water think of him affectionately as one of the world's best
comedians.

Sea otters live in colonies, sometimes huge ones, in and around
great beds of kelp that make islands offshore. They float on their
backs on the surface of the water to sleep or rest, each one
anchoring himself to the kelp by winding a ribbon of it around
his middle, so that he will not float away. They hide in the kelp
if their one dangerous enemy, the killer whale, comes near.

Floating on their backs is, in fact, one of the major occupa-
tions of sea otters. A mother otter will float and hold her baby
on her stomach while it nurses, plays, or rests; from here it learns
to swim and to float for itself. A feeding otter—and they eat
three meals a day—dives to the bottom and brings up a crab or
abalone or flounder or some other sea animal. Then he floats
and, using his tummy as a table, he pulls the animal to pieces and
eats it bit by bit—winding up by licking his "fingers"!

Once there were hundreds of thousands of these interesting
animals all along the Pacific Coast from the tip of the Aleutian
Islands to Baja California. From the first time man ever saw one
of them, he has coveted the fur as one of the softest, most beautiful, and most durable furs in the world. So, as America was settled and boats were improved, he slaughtered the sea otters,
young and adults alike, for the riches of their furs. Pelts sometimes sold for five hundred to one thousand dollars; the last one
to be sold legally, in London, brought nearly two thousand dollars.

By 1910 the catch had dropped from thousands each year to

a pitiful thirty-one; in 1911 killing them was prohibited by international treaty. The herds in Alaskan waters started then, slowly, to increase; today there may be five to six thousand northern sea otters, and it is hoped they are spreading east and south from their Aleutian colonies. Rebuilding the herds is a slow process, because only one baby, usually, is born at one time to a mother otter, and probably young are not born oftener than every two or three years. Yet the State of Alaska was able to harvest about five hundred sea otters in 1967 from state-owned areas, to begin a fur industry. If it can be developed, it will be very important to Alaska.

Down the coast, sea otters are gone from Washington and Oregon waters, and it was believed for years that the California sea otters had been wiped out too. But in 1938 they were rediscovered in Monterey Bay—a herd of nearly fifty, basking in the kelp! What an exciting day that was, for all who love animals! Of course this herd was carefully protected, under both Federal and California law, and more than six hundred southern sea otters have recently been counted off the California coast.

So here is an especially happy ending—the restoration of an interesting and valuable animal in its own natural habitat, when once it had apparently disappeared entirely. Today people can stand on the high headlands of the Pacific Coast mainland and watch the sea otters playing in the surf and in the nearby kelp beds.

Chapter 8

THE BALD EAGLE

"If I could see a bald eagle, I'd go home happy!" We looked at the speaker in surprise. Bald eagles in Florida Bay? We had never heard of such a thing! But this was our first trip to Florida, and it was quite evident we didn't know much about the state.

We were on a National Audubon Society boat, scanning sky and water through binoculars, as we threaded our way around the many mangrove islands in shallow Florida Bay. Birds we had seen in profusion—beautiful roseate spoonbills in flight, great white herons standing in the shallow water in solitary splendor, egrets and brown pelicans and ibis nesting together in great rookeries on some of the islands, fork-tailed frigate birds circling overhead. But we had not seen any bald eagles.

Suddenly our tour leader pointed to an island some distance ahead of us and a little to the left and said, "Put your glasses on that tall tree." And there sat a bald eagle, white head flashing in the sun! Majestic, beautiful, he was lord of all he surveyed— well, almost! We learned later that the female runs the household and has been known to scream at her mate for hours, like any nagging woman, if he does something to displease her.

If this eagle had a mate, she was away on business of her own, and soon he took off and sailed away on strong, powerful wings. As we watched him disappear, our tour leader told us that, except for Alaska, Florida has more bald eagles than any other

The female bald eagle sometimes screams angrily at her mate when he displeases her.

state. But even in these states, the number of bald eagles is decreasing every year. Maine is the only northeastern state where bald eagles still nest, and reproduction there is extremely low.

Many times, in our childhood on a ranch in the Colorado Rocky Mountains, we had watched a pair of bald eagles circling and circling, high overhead. We children were sure the eagles had a nest on a high, rocky cliff on a nearby mountain, but we had never been able to find it.

Although we had both sheep and calves on our ranch, our father had instructed our brothers never to shoot at an eagle, either a bald eagle or a golden one, and he also banned shooting most hawks and owls. He tried to persuade neighboring ranchers not to shoot at eagles, because, he said, they did more good than harm, by catching ground squirrels and mice and other rodents that destroyed the crops. The ranchers were afraid these huge birds of prey would kill their calves or carry off their lambs, but they had to admit that, so far, the eagles had never disturbed their livestock. Fortunately, in 1940 a federal law was passed protecting the bald eagle. This law did not apply in Alaska until 1959, however, and was not extended to the golden eagle until 1962.

AMERICA'S NATIONAL BIRD

It is beyond understanding why Congress waited so long to provide protection for our national bird. And it is hard to believe that we, the people of the United States, would allow the bald eagle, chosen as our national symbol because of his majesty and fierce independence, to be brought to the verge of extinction. His image appears on the Great Seal of the United States and on many state seals, on much of our currency and on many of our stamps. It is in the insignias of our armed forces and in those of the Boy Scouts, whose highest rating is Eagle Scout. Nevertheless, this great bird may soon become a thing of the past and take his place among other wildlife treasures that have been lost to us forever because of intolerance, greed, and indifference.

The bald eagle, our largest bird of prey except for the California condor, is truly native to North America. It has never been seen on any other continent except the northeast coast of Siberia, where it had apparently migrated from Alaska. It has appeared in practically all the states, but only as a migrant or winter resident in some of them. Bald eagles often migrate southward from extremely cold winter weather, and immature southern eagles have been found in northern states and Canada during the summer months. In general, bald eagles seem to prefer to live along sea coasts, lakes, or rivers, where their kind of food is most abundant.

The adult bald eagle is a striking-looking bird, with his handsome white head and spreading white tail, fierce yellow eyes and beak, and dark-brown body. The immature bird does not attain the white feathers on his head and tail until he is four or five years old, and is often mistaken for a golden eagle, which is all brown. However, the bald eagle has no feathers on the lower part of his leg, while the golden eagle is feathered clear to his feet.

The male bald eagle is somewhat smaller than the female, averaging about thirty-three inches in length, from tip of beak to end of tail, with a wingspread of about eighty-three inches. His mate exceeds him by several inches, in both length and wingspread. The southern eagle is slightly smaller than the northern one.

Bald eagles mate for life, but if one of a pair is killed, the other eagle usually takes a new mate. They prefer to build their nests in tall trees, the taller the better, but will nest in a smaller tree or on a high cliff if there is not a suitable tree in the area. They will also nest on the ground in treeless areas. The nest is a large, ungainly mass of sticks and small limbs. The inside of it has a nearly flat surface, composed of clods of dirt and soft vegetation and surrounded by a rim of sticks. Bald eagles tend to use the same nest year after year, adding new material each year, so that, finally, the nest becomes enormous, and may crash of its own weight. One such nest, in Ohio, was used for thirty-six years and grew to be twelve feet high and eight and a half feet across the top, before it was blow down by a storm. A nest in St. Petersburg, Florida, was twenty feet high and ten feet across.

In Florida the average time of egg laying is early winter, while in the middle Atlantic coastal states it is March and April, and, in Alaska, in mid-May. Two eggs are laid, rarely three, and they hatch in about thirty-four days.

At first the nestlings are covered with a soft, white down, which changes to a dark-gray down before the feathers start to grow. Both parents take food to the nest and cut it into small pieces before feeding it to the nestlings. Before leaving the nest, in ten to thirteen weeks, the eaglets preen and exercise and flex their wings, in preparation for flying. Even after leaving the nest, they will often stay around it, and the parent birds will feed them, for several weeks.

The favorite food of the bald eagle is fish, which he snatches from the water with his claws or finds dead along the shore. Sometimes he robs an osprey of its catch, harassing the smaller bird until it drops the fish and then snatching the fish in midair. He is seldom fast enough to catch a live duck, but sometimes he catches injured or sick ducks or other waterfowl. Often he finds dead ones that have been overlooked by hunters or that have died from poisoning. Although the bald eagle is a scavenger, he likes his meat as fresh as possible.

On the western plains and in the mountains, where the supply of fish is limited, he catches rabbits and ground squirrels and other small rodents. He may feed on dead cattle and sheep, and the carcasses of large wild animals, such as deer and antelope. He might carry off a very small lamb or fawn, but weight-lifting experiments with captive eagles showed that they could not lift more than a few pounds. In Alaska the bald eagle feeds on birds as well as fish; in the Aleutian Islands, sea birds make up most of his diet.

Man is almost the only enemy of the bald eagle, and a terrible enemy he has been!

In spite of the fact that the bald eagle is our national bird, a bounty was paid on him in Alaska for many years, and more than one hundred thousand bald eagles were killed and the bounty collected during a period of about thirty-four years. In 1952 a regulation was adopted providing that bald eagles "may be killed

These bald-eagle nestlings will not have white heads and tails for several years.

⌈only when committing damage to fishes, other wildlife, and domestic birds and animals." A few months later the eagle bounty
law was repealed; and when Alaska entered the Union in 1959,
the new state came under the federal law that forbids the killing
⌊of bald eagles.

Hunters have continued to shoot bald eagles, regardless of the
laws protecting them. In 1962, one hundred and eighteen dead
eagles were found, of which ninety-one were shot. Some of these
were immature birds and may have been mistaken for golden
eagles and killed before the law was passed that same year to
protect those birds.

A number of factors have tended to reduce the eagle population in Florida—irresponsible hunters, land developments that take
over the eagles' nesting areas, hurricanes that destroy the nests,
and, it is feared, the wide use of pesticides. Many scientists believe that pesticides used on farms and for mosquito control drain
off into the rivers and bays and contaminate the fish; when eagles
eat the fish, they may be poisoned or their eggs may be infertile.
This belief is strengthened by the fact that the poisons have been
found in the tissues of dead eagles that have been examined; and
many nests are found with infertile eggs or no eggs at all.

Many people are at work to save the bald eagle from extinction. The Patuxent Wildlife Research Center is performing au-
topsies on the bodies of eagles found dead and sent to them, in an
attempt to learn more about the eagles and why they died, including the effects of pesticides on them. The wing and tail
feathers from these bodies are sent to the Southwestern Indian
tribes which have long used eagle feathers for ceremonial pur-
poses. This helps to discourage illegal shooting by market hunters
for sale to the Indians.

For several years the National Audubon Society has carried on
a widespread study, called the Continental Bald Eagle Project,
to learn about the number and distribution of bald eagles in the

United States and also about their habits. The purpose of this study is to work out an effective program to save them from extinction. The Society is also waging an active publicity campaign to let all the people in the United States know about the plight of their national bird. State and local Audubon societies and other organizations interested in wildlife conservation are aiding in this work.

The Florida Audubon Society, at Maitland, Florida, is carrying on an especially active and successful crusade in behalf of the southern bald eagle. Its youth organization, called Eagle Guardians, with membership cards and pins, now has more than twenty thousand members.

Another successful project of the Florida Society is the two million-acre Kissimmee Cooperative Bald Eagle Sanctuary, which was established under the leadership of George Heinzman and his wife to protect the eagles nesting in Florida's central prairie lands. The owners of these lands have signed pledges to protect the eagles and nests on their lands from shooting, nest-robbing, or undue disturbances. They do not destroy trees containing active nests, and have promised, when clearing the land, to leave some tall trees, wherever practical, for possible future use by eagles.

The vast Everglades National Park offers another haven to the Florida bald eagle, and the number of immature birds is gradually increasing in this area. There are now about sixty-five active nests in the Park.

All over the country, other government agencies such as the United States Forest Service and the Bureau of Sports Fisheries and Wildlife are using great care in the lands they manage, to prevent destruction or damage to the nesting areas of the bald eagle. Big land-holding companies, too, such as timber and power companies, are protecting the eagles' nests. In northern Minnesota, Chippewa Indians have placed a half-million-acre reservation under a bald-eagle protection program. So there are millions of acres in the United States where bald eagles can nest in protected areas.

OTHER BIRDS OF PREY IN DANGER

Another bird of prey that has become rare is the American peregrine falcon, or duck hawk. This falcon nests from northern Alaska to southern Greenland and also in western Mexico and the United States, as far east as Colorado and western Texas. It once nested in the eastern states, too, but its nests are no longer found

This osprey is bringing a fish to her nestlings. The nest is built in the

there. It winters throughout the United States and as far south
as Argentina.

The peregrine falcon is fifteen to nineteen inches long; the
wings are long and pointed, with a spread of three to four feet,
and the tail is narrow. Like most birds of prey, the female is
larger than the male. The adult bird has a dark, slate-colored
back and wings, a black cap, and a light breast and throat. Black
feathers on each cheek resemble a heavy mustache. The immature falcon has a brown back and wings.

The falcon does not build a nest, but usually lays its eggs—

top of a clump of young mangroves.

three or four—on a sheltered cliff ledge. It has found city life to its liking, too, and sometimes uses high window ledges on city skyscrapers for nesting sites.

The peregrine falcon flies with incredible speed and preys largely on smaller birds. He strikes in the air, killing his victim with one blow and sending it hurtling to earth. Usually the falcon follows it down to the ground, but if the bird is small, he may catch it in midair. Like other falcons, he seems to take delight in pestering larger birds in the air, diving at them and flying around them.

Because of his speed, the peregrine has been used in the ancient sport of falconry in the Old World for many centuries. This sport and the fad of keeping birds of prey for pets are becoming increasingly popular in America and may become a real threat to the birds. Most experienced falconers will not do anything that threatens the birds of prey, but market hunters are not so conservation-minded. Supplying pet stores and falconers with birds of prey has become big business for them, and they are taking young birds from the nests and trapping the adults in growing numbers.

Thoughtless hunters and farmers are still shooting peregrines, along with other birds of prey, but the greatest threat to them may be the widespread use of pesticides. As in the case of eagles, pesticides are probably killing the birds directly or causing their eggs to be infertile.

The American osprey, too, may soon be on our threatened list because of pesticides. These handsome fish hawks—they eat nothing but fish—build their nests in trees, on top of poles, and sometimes even on the ground. Like the eagle, the osprey adds to its nest year after year until it becomes a huge pile of sticks and various articles that the osprey has picked up and worked into the nest.

Farmers are fond of the fish hawk because it chases crows and other birds away from the area where its nest is located; so they often put up platforms for it to nest on near their cornfields. On the Atlantic Coast, some farmers put cartwheels on top of poles. In some places along the coast, the ospreys caused trouble by nesting on the power poles, until the power companies put up duplicate poles for them, with platforms on top and sticks for nests.

However, the number of ospreys nesting along the Atlantic coast, as well as around the Great Lakes, is rapidly diminishing, and scientists are again blaming pesticides in the bodies of the fish on which the ospreys feed.

Guy Coheleach

Chapter 9

NOWHERE TO LIVE

In 1950, one hundred and fifty million people lived in the United States. Today over two hundred million live here. At this rate of increase, another thirty years will add another hundred million—will more than double our population of 1950.

Still, we have more than three and a half million square miles of land in this country. Striking an average of people and land, we have about sixty persons for every square mile—compared, for instance, with Japan, where there are 585 persons per square mile!

It would seem, then, that we in the United States should have plenty of land for people, and plenty left over for the various kinds of animals that live naturally on this land. But we don't. Land, and the water that must go with it, are today among our scarcest commodities.

So the big question is, how shall the land be used? For farming? For forests? For cities? For national parks and wilderness areas? For housing developments? For highways? For recreation? For factories and other industry? For wildlife? All of these factors of living, and still others, need some part of the land. How much should each one have?

The ivory-bill, our biggest woodpecker, may survive. Although for years he was thought to be extinct he was recently seen in Texas. He is marked by broad bands on folded wings, and by his heavy bill. He became almost homeless when forests were cut and old, dead trees removed.

We don't know the answer; and the right answer in one part of the country might be the wrong one in another. But we're becoming more and more aware of one big mistake we've been making. We've been allowing wildlife to wind up, too often, where it is in these questions—at the end of the list.

So today big timber companies and United States government agencies work together to preserve trees that offer home and food to a handsome but very rare woodpecker. Bird breeders around the world have helped snatch Hawaii's native goose from extinction. And man is protecting many other species to the best of his ability while he studies them to learn their habitat requirements.

THE IVORY-BILLED WOODPECKER

Wonderful news for people interested in wildlife is a recent announcement that field workers for the U.S. Fish and Wildlife Service have seen several pairs of ivory-billed woodpeckers. There had been no official sightings of this big bird for more than fifteen years, and most ornithologists thought that he was probably extinct. But now he has been seen in the Neches River valley in the Big Thicket country of eastern Texas—has been identified there beyond any doubt.

The ivory-bill is the largest woodpecker in the United States. He is second in size in North America only to Mexico's closely related imperial ivory-bill. At a whopping twenty-one inches long, compare him with our little downy, at seven inches!

He is the victim of man's taking over the swamps and forests in the south. Once this big fellow was a resident of most of the southeastern states, in the cypress swamps and forests of gum and oak. But he was never as common, even in early days, as he seemed to be, because the somewhat similar pileated woodpecker was often mistaken for him.

Both birds are black and white, with a big red crest (the female ivory-bill's crest is black). But when they are at rest or climbing a tree, it is fairly easy to tell one bird from the other. A broad white patch shows on the ivory-bill's wings, while the pileated's folded wings seem nearly all black. And of course the big, strong, ivory-colored bill is the "trademark" of the rare woodpecker.

Here is a bird that has a very limited bill of fare. He lives on grubs of the wood-boring insects that work beneath the bark of dead or dying trees, stripping off the bark of the trees to get at them. So he depends on a supply of old trees in forest or swamp—and these have disappeared rapidly, as man logged off the forests and drained the swamps.

There may be other areas in the south where the big bird still lives. A number of unofficial observers have reported sighting him at various points—along the Congaree River in South Carolina, the Tombigbee River in Alabama and Mississippi, the Altamaha River in Georgia, and the Apalachicola River in Florida.

To try to protect the few remaining birds, the Fish and Wildlife Service is working with timber companies in these areas to save some of the trees that the woodpecker needs. Stories of the birds' presence and their rarity have been widely published, so that hunters and nature lovers will protect them. Perhaps someday a sanctuary or refuge may protect a suitable habitat, and a few of the big ivory-bills may continue to live.

THE WOOD STORK

The wood stork is shaped so much like an ibis that for years he got himself called "wood ibis," and often still is called that. But when wood storks perch in the tops of cypress or mangrove trees, they look very much like the flocks of storks on Dutch roofs that are so often pictured. They are the only kind of stork that we have in the United States.

A wood stork is a big, ungainly bird, standing probably three to four feet tall—twice the size of an ibis. He is black and white, with a bare black neck and head and a long, tapering, heavy bill. He has a black tail and broad black bands along the trailing edges of his wings; his body and much of his wings are gleaming white.

Flying, there is nothing ungainly about him. His long neck and bill stretching ahead and his long legs trailing behind make a straight, slim line; his great wings spread to five feet or more as he flaps them powerfully to speed along at thirty-five miles an hour, or—which he seems to greatly prefer—holds them wide to glide for miles.

A small flock may move along quickly, perhaps in the evening, from feeding grounds to roost; they fly bunched up, or in a line, or perhaps in a "V". But often the birds soar in great flocks that rise and wheel, rise and wheel, in rising currents of warm air. As they glide, first the half-black undersides of the wings will be turned earthward, and they will seem dark. Then, in unison, the birds turn, and the shining white catches the sun. So there is a flashing, all together, of dark, then white, then dark, then white again, always in unison and going on and on until the birds are so high that they are out of sight.

Wood storks raise their young in great colonies, called rookeries. Thousands of pairs may nest in a rookery, filling the tops
of trees with big, loose nests built of sticks. Their favorite nesting
areas in America have always been on the islands of mangrove
trees in Everglades National Park, and in the cypress swamps of
southern Florida, where tall, craggy trees stand close together
and shallow, fresh-water lakes and ponds nearby give the birds
plenty of fish to eat. Probably more than one hundred thousand
storks nested in Florida as recently as 1930.

Nesting time, between late November and May, is a strenuous
period in the life of a pair of wood storks. From the time the first
egg is laid (there are usually four), the two birds take turns at
the nest. While one broods the eggs, keeping them warm and
protecting them, the other flies to the feeding grounds and eats.
Its food is largely fish, from minnow size to six inches long, together with whatever crayfish, worms, water insects, and other
small animal life it can stir up. And "stir up" is right: Balancing
with its wings, the bird wades through water up to a foot deep,
its bill under water while it stirs the mud with one foot. When

*Wood storks fill the tops of
trees in a rookery on an island in Everglades National
Park. Several thousand birds
may nest in a single rookery.*

fish or crayfish darts ahead of the stirring, the wood stork grabs it.

Several pounds of food a day are needed by each bird, so that most of the time away from the nest must be spent in feeding. When the eggs hatch, in about a month, the work doubles and redoubles, because the parents must bring food to the young birds until they are about ten weeks old. Someone has estimated that a rookery with six thousand pairs of birds will use more than two and a half million pounds of fish in a season—all of it carried from the fresh water of shallow lakes and ponds. Clearly, there must be large fresh-water areas near a wood stork rookery.

With the many changes that have come to Florida in recent years, the wood stork has lost much of both his nesting areas and his feeding grounds. Lumbering took down most of the big cypress trees; draining took much of the fresh water.

By 1957 the hundred thousand storks of Florida had dropped to an estimated eight thousand. Since then, drought and hurricanes and other storms have added to man's activities, to drastically reduce the stork population.

There are still three big rookeries where thousands of pairs of storks can nest, and where it is hoped they may always nest successfully. One of these is the Audubon Society's Corkscrew Swamp Sanctuary in southern Florida, a cypress swamp. The others are in the southern part of Everglades National Park, on mangrove islands in salt water, from which the birds fly an average of fifteen or twenty miles to fresh-water feeding grounds.

But even here, they may not survive. The feeding grounds of Corkscrew are threatened by drainage. And there have been very dry years in which the storks built no nests at all, and others in which the young birds were killed by storms or starved in their nests because the feeding grounds dried up. But one year, in which thousands of nestlings in Corkscrew Swamp were killed by a January freeze, three thousand parent birds came back to the nests and produced a second brood!

The storks have demonstrated that they have wonderful stay-
ing power—that after a bad year, they can come back in numbers. So we can hope, in these three refuges, at least, to have new
generations of wood storks in the years to come.

BIRDS IN THE HAWAIIAN ISLANDS

From big Hawaii (more than four thousand square miles) to

*The nene goose, state bird of Hawaii, barely escaped extinction. In the
wild it lives in Hawaii's national parks.*

tiny Laysan (about seven hundred acres), the Hawaiian Islands have a full share of beautiful and interesting birds. The islands are spaced along a line almost two thousand miles long, and so each one is likely to be far distant from any other land. Yet each one has its land birds, often in striking tropical plumage.

But today this wealth is far less than it was in earlier years. When improved ships began to ride the vast Pacific, visitors and new residents came to these native-inhabited islands, "crossroads of the world." They brought with them cats, dogs, rats, and mongooses; all of these killed adult birds and ate the eggs and young. And men planted great areas of sugar cane, pineapple, and other crops, and brought in cattle, clearing away woodlands and grasslands and draining wetlands that were the birds' natural habitats. The newcomers also introduced birds with diseases against which the Hawaiian birds had no resistance; and they introduced mosquitoes that carried the diseases from one bird to another.

So the bird life of Hawaii suffered. Many species were quickly wiped out. In a number of others, only a few birds are still living.

There is the Kauai akialoa, a yellow bird about the size of a bluebird, with a long, curved bill with which it sips nectar from flowers. It was once fairly common in the forests of the island of Kauai; today there are only a few, or may be none at all. Once the ou, lovely small songbird with a bright yellow head, lived on all the major islands; today only a few can be found, and those only on Kauai and Hawaii. The ooaa, whose bright yellow feathers brought fabulous prices, had four subspecies, each on its separate island; today only the Kauai oo survives, and it is so rare that it may be gone too. There are many like these, endangered, probably gone. Included are Hawaii's only hawk, the ii; and only crow, the alala, reduced to a few of each one, on the island of Hawaii.

But one of the exciting news stories of the year tells of the rediscovery, on the island of Maui, of the Maui nukupuu (pro-nounced *Maw*-ee noo-koo-*poo*-oo), a bird that was last seen more than seventy years ago and had long been considered extinct. The nukupuu is a small, perching bird with a long, down-curving bill and a tubular tongue with which it extracts nectar from flowers. Several pairs were discovered in the Valley of the Seven Sacred Pools, a lovely mountain area with more than a hundred waterfalls. Three other kinds of very rare birds were seen in the same locality—crested honeycreepers, Maui creepers, and Maui parrotbills. The valley is almost undisturbed, and the Nature Conservancy and the U.S. Department of the Interior, who co-sponsored the expedition that discovered the birds, are acquiring it for a park where they will be protected.

Happier, too, is the story of Hawaii's state bird, the nene goose (pronounced nay-nay). Once there were twenty-five thousand of these handsome geese living on the islands of Hawaii and Maui —and nowhere else in the world. They lived on the mountain slopes of old volcanoes, at an altitude of five to eight thousand feet, and were away from water for so long that their feet lost the full webbing of a water-habitat goose.

They were easy to kill because they are very tame, and they are delicious to eat. So they were slaughtered by market hunters who came to the islands. Not until this century, when their number had dropped to less than fifty, was the alarm sounded that the species was in danger, and hunting them was stopped by law.

Even so, the nene could easily have been lost. But a pair was given to a Hawaiian rancher, who guarded them well and pro-duced a fine flock from them. A few of these were sent to the Severn Wildfowl Trust, breeder of rare birds in England, where a flock of several hundred was developed. From these beginnings, state agencies and individuals in Hawaii and other states received a few of the nene and built up additional flocks. All of these have produced enough birds so that nearly three hundred have been returned to the wild, volcanic mountains in the national parks of Hawaii and Maui, and are thriving there. Several hundred more still live in the captive flocks.

So here is a fine bird that has probably been saved, and into his protection have gone international efforts—help from England, help from the World Wildlife Fund and national and international foundations, help from the United States and from Hawaii and other states, and help from individuals. So the nene is truly an international bird as well as Hawaii's own.

There are happy endings too for the stories of the Laysan honeycreeper or finch, and the Laysan duck. These are two of five birds that once lived on tiny Laysan and nowhere else in the world. About fifty years ago, visitors took rabbits to the island; the rabbits multiplied so rapidly that they ate up all the vegetation—and starved themselves out. The bird life died out too, and three kinds were gone for good. But the duck and the finch, down to only a few of each, managed to survive to the time when the rabbits were gone and the vegetation had come back.

The finch quickly increased its numbers as the vegetation grew, and it is now quite common on the island. A lovely singer, it is Laysan's only songbird. The island is now part of the Hawaiian Islands National Wildlife Refuge, and so the bird is protected, even though its home is very remote from the larger islands.

The Laysan duck, about the size of a teal, prospered also and its growing numbers are carefully protected in its homeland, where there are now about five hundred; about one hundred more were bred in captivity. Measures are under way to transplant it to other islands, so that, if some accident happened to it on Laysan, the whole stock would not be wiped out.

The National Wildlife Refuge includes most of the small islands that lie in a long chain northwest of Kauai. Another recently established area where birds are protected and the alteration of their habitat is prohibited, is the ten-thousand-acre Alakai Swamp

Wilderness Preserve on Kauai, operated by the state of Hawaii. It is hoped that through these and other protective agencies, some of Hawaii's endangered birds will be saved.

PRAIRIE DOGS

Buffalo cropped the grass on either side, as we drove along the road in Wind Cave National Park, and we saw pronghorn ante-

Prairie dogs have lost their homes to man's plow and his grazing cattle.

lope in the distance. But no people! Except for the animals, we seemed to be alone on this prairie land, which spread out as far as the eye could see.

Then, suddenly, as we stopped watching the animals and glanced down the road ahead of us, we saw the people—a crowd of them, watching something near the road. We pulled up behind a ranger's truck at the end of a long line of cars and asked the ranger what they were looking at.

"A prairie-dog town," he said, laughing. "Those dogs attract more attention than all the other animals in the park!"

Of course we walked over to have a look too—and stayed for an hour, watching the antics of these funny little animals. Like most wildlife in the parks, they have become accustomed to people and so went about their own affairs, paying little attention to any of us. Some were putting fresh earth on the cone-shaped mounds around the mouths of their burrows and packing it down with their front feet. Others were standing upright on their mounds, or feeding on nearby vegetation, or running back and forth between burrows.

Sometimes, when two prairie dogs met, they put their noses together, as if kissing; sometimes they groomed each other's fur. Often they would utter the strange little "bark" that gave them their name, because it reminded early settlers of a yipping dog. When a golden eagle or a hawk sailed over, one of them, perhaps a lookout, gave a quite different, warning cry, and all of them scurried into their burrows, where they waited for the all-clear signal.

Once the interior of North America was a vast area of tall- and mid-grass prairies and short-grass plains. Great herds of bison roamed these grasslands and shared the bountiful feed with millions, probably billions, of this small, yellowish brown prairie dog, which is really a rodent belonging to the squirrel family.

He has short legs and short ears and the end of his tail is black.

When he builds his elaborate, underground home, he digs into the ground with the sharp claws on his front feet; then he kicks the dirt backward out of the burrow with his hind feet. The entrance to the burrow is about eight inches in diameter at the surface, but the hole soon narrows to about five inches, and then it drops straight down for three to fifteen feet. The prairie dog usually makes a shelf or niche a short distance below the entrance, where he can sit and look around before he ventures out.

Several side tunnels branch off from the entry hole, with small, round rooms at the end of each. One of these is lined with soft, dried grass and weeds, and here, in March or April, four to six babies are born, blind and naked. In a few weeks, however, their bodies will be covered with hair, and they will open their eyes. Soon thereafter, they will be able to come above ground and learn to eat grass and other plants with their elders.

The black-tailed prairie dog has some white-tailed cousins,

This rare weasel, the black-footed ferret, is the prairie dogs' natural enemy.

who live in higher altitudes and do not gather in such large colonies as the black-tails. One white-tailed species, the Utah prairie dog, is found in only five counties in Utah and is considered very rare.

But it was the black-tail that lived in such numbers with the buffalo and with the plains Indians who called this vast area their home. The black-tails lived in "towns" that covered many square miles and contained millions of prairie dogs. One such town, in Texas, was said to cover twenty-five thousand square miles and to shelter four hundred million "dogs."

Then the white man came and killed the buffalo and drove out the Indians. He plowed up the fertile tall-grass prairies and planted them to corn and wheat. And his domestic cattle replaced the buffalo on the short-grass, semi-arid plains. The prairie dogs continued to eat the grass, as well as the new crops, and sometimes a cow or a horse stepped into a burrow and broke its leg. So the prairie dogs had to go too.

It took a long time to get rid of them; but "rodent control" was launched against them in a campaign of poison and gas, and it almost wiped them out. Today you will find prairie-dog towns in only a few places—Wind Cave National Park, Devils Tower National Monument, Wichita Mountains Wildlife Refuge, the city park at Lubbock, Texas, and a few other parks and refuges, where they are protected. An effort is being made, also, to protect the white-tailed species in Utah; rodent-control personnel have been instructed not to kill this species.

THE BLACK-FOOTED FERRET

The widespread destruction of the prairie dog brought other animals to the brink of extinction, because they depended on the prairie-dog towns for food and lodging. One of these, the black-footed ferret, is the rarest mammal in North America.

Not much is known about this animal, one of the larger mem-

When prairie dogs went, so did the black-footed ferret. He depends on them for his food, and often for his lodging.

The burrowing owl, like the ferret, often uses a prairie-dog hole for his home—whether or not it is occupied by the prairie dog.

bers of the weasel family, because he is shy and wary and comes out mostly at night. Apparently the species was never very abundant. Audubon described and painted him in 1851, but no one else saw him for many years, and some naturalists accused Audubon of "faking" his painting.

The home of the black-footed ferret seems to be largely in prairie-dog towns, where he is a most unwelcome guest; he preys on the prairie dogs for his food, and finds shelter in their burrows. Although he is nearly two feet long, he is slim and agile, and has no trouble threading his way along the corridors of the prairie dogs' underground homes.

He is a striking-looking animal—buffy yellow shading to darker brown on his back and the top of his head. His feet and the tip of his tail are black, and he wears a black mask across his eyes.

At one time he probably ranged throughout North America's vast grasslands and in the Rocky Mountains as well, wherever prairie-dog towns existed. Now the few remaining ferrets live almost entirely in several counties in South Dakota, and these few are still threatened by the continued poisoning of the prairie dogs. Occasionally one is killed on the highway or shot by people hunting prairie dogs for sport, although there is a law in South Dakota against killing them.

A study of the black-footed ferret is under way by the Bureau of Sport Fisheries and Wildlife, in cooperation with the National Park Service and the South Dakota Department of Fish, Wildlife and Parks, to learn how this animal can best be protected. Efforts are being made to establish him in the national parks and wildlife refuges where prairie-dog towns exist.

THE BURROWING OWL

The comical little western burrowing owl is another victim of agricultural development and prairie-dog "control," for he, too, depends on the prairie-dog towns for shelter. He can be found in most of the states west of the Mississippi, but he is rapidly diminishing with the destruction of the prairie dog.

This small, light-brown owl, about nine inches long, has a short tail and unusually long legs for an owl. He is most often seen sitting on the ground or on a fence post, and has a funny habit of bobbing and bowing his head, first to one side and then the other, especially when alarmed.

The burrowing owl is perfectly able to dig his own burrow, but he seems to prefer the deserted burrow of a prairie dog. In fact, a colony of a dozen or more owls will take up residence in a prairie-dog town. Each pair of owls builds its round nest at the end of a burrow, five to ten feet from the entrance. The nest is lined with grass and hair and bits of dried cow and horse dung, and five to nine eggs are laid in it. The baby owls are strong enough to come out of the burrow when they are about three weeks old.

This owl feeds largely on insects, mice and other very small rodents, frogs, and small birds. He is beneficial to the farmer because he eats so many mice and grasshoppers. Now and then he eats baby prairie dogs, and the adult "dogs" occasionally retaliate by eating the owls' eggs.

There is a subspecies of the burrowing owl in the prairie land of central Florida. It has been separated so long from its western relatives that it has become slightly different. It is somewhat darker in color, and it digs its own burrow. This little owl, like the western one, sometimes tempts a "sportsman" to take a "pot shot" at it as it sits fearlessly on a fence post.

THE PRAIRIE CHICKEN

Prairie chickens have always ranked high among America's game birds. About half as large as a turkey, they were—and still are—fun to hunt and good to eat. But once there were so many

that hunting took the form of a contest of "Who can kill the most?" Hunters, breaking camp, often left great piles of them—too many to use. And market hunters killed so many that one New York poultry market received twenty tons in a single day.

Along with this slaughter, man was moving in and taking over the prairie chickens' habitat. He was plowing up the prairie, wiping out the tall-grass prairies, especially, where the birds lived and made their nests.

First victim was the heath hen, a prairie chicken of the eastern

The sac on the side of the male prairie chicken's neck will swell to great size when he "booms"—a sound he makes by beating his wings.

states that became extinct in 1932. Faring not much better is a close relative in the South, Attwater's prairie chicken. Once a million or more of these birds lived in the coastal prairies of Texas and Louisiana—vast stretches of tall-grass prairies spreading inland from the Gulf of Mexico. Now there are probably only five hundred to seven hundred and fifty birds left. Most of these are in a 3500-acre tract of land in southwestern Texas, set aside as a refuge for them. And in a recent gift of 7,162 acres to the Aransas Wildlife Refuge, there are extensive grasslands that are excellent habitat for these prairie chickens and will be managed for them. They are protected from hunting wherever they live.

This bird and the heath hen are both subspecies of the greater prairie chicken. A third subspecies, the northern prairie chicken, lives in scattered prairie areas through the middle west, the plains states, and southern Canada. Living in somewhat the same areas is a different species, the lesser prairie chicken, a bird that is slightly smaller but very similar.

In some states, hunting either of these northern birds is prohibited; in others, where they are more numerous, limited hunting is allowed. But both kinds are rare and both continue to be threatened as more and more grasslands are taken by man for some other purpose. In some states—in Illinois, for example—efforts are being made to preserve areas of grassland where the prairie chickens are known to be living. The World Wildlife Fund is acquiring land in Texas for a similar sanctuary. And it is possible that a Grasslands National Park will be created in the plains where prairie chickens live.

Many observers report the prairie chicken as one of our most interesting birds. It is the strange "boomer" that in the spring and fall makes a booming sound heard a mile away. The males gather at a "booming ground"—a ridge or mound higher than the land around, and make the sound by beating the air with their wings. They have yellow sacs on each side of the neck, which they inflate to a remarkable size. They lift and spread their tails and the tall tufts of feathers on their necks, and stamp their feet and strut as if they owned the earth.

Prairie chickens nest in clumps of grass and build and line their nests with grass. Each hen may lay as many as a dozen eggs, and if her nest is broken up before the eggs hatch, she may nest again in that season. The baby birds grow quickly to a size where they are independent of their mothers. So biologists believe that if some habitat is saved for these birds, they, too, will be saved.

THE BIGHORN SHEEP

Here is an animal, shy and wary of man, harming no one, seeking as its home some of the most rugged and inaccessible of all our land. It eats grass and browse plants and has no serious enemies in its natural world; it is able to see for long distances, and so an enemy does not often succeed in approaching a herd of bighorns.

So one might think that here is an animal with no problems. Yet, of the five subspecies of bighorns that America recently had, one, the Badlands bighorn of North and South Dakota, is already extinct. And two others, both living in California, are rare. One of these, the California bighorn, lives in the high Sierra Mountains and in the mountains of western Canada. The other, the peninsular bighorn, lives in the southwestern mountains of California and in the Baja California peninsula. There are only a few hundred of each kind.

The desert bighorn of the Southwest is estimated to be several thousand strong; and between eight and ten thousand Rocky Mountain bighorns live in small herds that are widely scattered through the Rocky Mountain states. Some of these states allow restricted hunting where the bighorns are most numerous; but the bighorns of California have been protected for many years. Why is protection necessary? Why are the bighorns decreasing, or, at best, only holding their own? A major reason is that man is moving into their habitat with his domestic sheep. The sheep not only compete for grass and other plants, leaving a reduced amount of food for the bighorns; they also carried a disease, scabies, to the bighorns, and many died from it.

The bighorns, sturdy as they may seem, actually have a rather precarious hold on life, specially as lambs. The lambs are very susceptible to pneumonia, and many, particularly in high mountain altitudes, die of it each year. Since only one baby, if any, is born to a mother bighorn each year, this toll among lambs is by itself a serious threat.

This husky Rocky Mountain bighorn ram, photographed in Colorado, would seem to have a good chance for survival. But as the years go by, there are fewer and fewer bighorns.

Add to that the bighorn's way of life: He goes high into the mountains in the summer, seeking the best forage and building up his body for the winter. Against winter's deep snows, he may return to lower meadows and hillsides, but even these do not offer the nourishment of his summer diet. So winter may be almost starvation time for him.

Now suppose that domestic sheep, driven in big herds into the highest mountain meadows for summer range, have used up some of the bighorns' summer food—and they use up winter range in the same way. Other animals, too, compete for food—deer and elk, antelope and rodents of various kinds. So the bighorns are undernourished, and they become easy victims of spreading disease.

National parks and wilderness areas are good for the bighorns. It is possible that, before we entirely lose this interesting animal, we will be able to make enough room to give him his necessary habitat.

Chapter 10

FISH IN DANGER

When you think "fish," what do you think of? Pets in a gold-fish bowl, or tiny, flashing, tropical gems in an aquarium? Or a frying-pan full of trout, just caught from stream or lake and browning over a fire for breakfast in camp? Or a monster caught in the open sea and hung up on the dock for all to see and admire?

What a great variety of fish there is in America! Outward from the shores, through salt water, there are almost unlimited kinds, many, perhaps, as yet unidentified—unnamed. The quantity, too, is enormous. It is very difficult to imagine that America might ever "run out" of salt-water fish.

Yet what we know about them is very little. Look at tuna, for instance—a mainstay of our salt-water commercial fisheries. How many are there? How many are caught each year? How fast do they renew themselves? What are their habits, their requirements? What else kills them besides man catching them? We are only beginning to learn the answers to these questions. Without them, in spite of the present abundant supply of tuna, we can use up the supply faster than it is replenished—and so someday have no tuna.

In fresh water—in lakes and rivers and smaller streams—the situation is already critical. Here the extent of the water is not the almost unlimited reaches of an ocean. Here there are the encircling shores of a lake, however large it may be; here there are the

Salmon can leap most natural waterfalls in streams, but man's dams are often too high and dry for leaping.

confining banks of a river. So here, if fish are taken in great quantities, the supply can be reduced very much more rapidly than in an ocean. Or, if the river or lake is changed, certain kinds of fish may die. If the water is polluted, the fish may die.

We in America are seeing these things happen to many kinds of our fresh-water fish—to giant fish that can grow more than ten feet long and weigh hundreds of pounds; to tiny miniatures no more than an inch long. The United States Fish and Wildlife Service lists twenty-four species of our fish that are in danger of extinction, and fourteen more that are rare; forty-five others are listed as uncertain and in need of more study. So nearly one hundred species of our fresh-water fish may today be in danger.

Some are important to commercial fisheries, some to sports fishing. Others have only a few individuals in an isolated pool or stream, and are of interest because, once gone, they will never be seen again.

WHAT HAPPENED TO OUR STURGEON?

Sturgeon are the largest fish that have ever been seen in fresh water. Their eggs supply most of the world's caviar, a topnotch delicacy even at the tables of royalty. They are called a "living fossil," because they have come down to us through a hundred million years of the earth's history. They were huge and abundant in American streams and lakes a hundred years ago. But now they are small and rare—unknown in many places where once they were common.

A sturgeon—any kind of sturgeon—is a remarkable fish. Most fish have a backbone made up of vertebrae, but a sturgeon has a flexible tube of cartilage; his whole skeleton, in fact, is more cartilage than bone. Instead of scales on the outside of his skin, he has heavy, bony plates—a row of them down the middle of his back and two rows along each side.

He eats all kinds of small water animals—shrimps, clams, snails,

This drawing of a twelve-foot Atlantic sturgeon is one of the few pictures we have of the big fish that were made from a live specimen. It was drawn in 1894 for the U.S. National Museum, from a specimen caught in the Potomac River. The short line at the right represents one foot.

crayfish, crabs, small fish—anything he can find on the bottom of river, lake, or ocean. But he does not stalk his prey. He moves slowly along on the bottom and lets a little cluster of fleshy whiskers, near his mouth, find food for him. When the whiskers touch anything alive, his mouth instantly shoots out and sucks it up. He has no teeth; the sucker mouth and a grinder-stomach do all the work of catching and chewing his food. Because of their feeding habits, sturgeon are rather sluggish, moving slowly from one locality to another.

They grow slowly, too. Perhaps they are a half inch long when they hatch from the eggs; it will be twelve to twenty years before they are three to four feet long and laying eggs themselves. They live for many years after they begin to spawn, and they continue to grow. Those of some of the larger species may live for one hundred and fifty years or more.

Giant among the sturgeons—and not an American fish—is the huge beluga, in the Caspian and Black seas and the Volga River. This big fellow holds the world's record at 28 feet long and 2860 pounds. Belugas and some other Eurasian species often weigh more than a thousand pounds, and they are today the principal source of canned and smoked sturgeon meat and caviar. The larger females have up to five million eggs—two hundred to three hundred pounds of caviar in one fish!

Of America's big sturgeons, the Atlantic, or sea sturgeon, were once common along the Atlantic coast. They were often ten feet long and weighed five hundred pounds or more; one recorded in New England was eighteen feet long; another, in Canada, fourteen feet. In early spring they went in great runs up the big rivers to spawn. When sturgeon spawn, they do not die as salmon do, but drift back to the sea. After two or more years, they may spawn again. The young fish that hatch from the eggs may live in the river a year or two before they drift down to the sea. So sturgeon of various sizes were common in our eastern rivers at almost any season, in America's early years.

In the Great Lakes, too, and in big midwestern rivers—the Mississippi, the Missouri, the Ohio—there were sturgeon. These, the lake, or rock, sturgeon, are a different species from those in the Atlantic. They are fresh-water fish, growing to eight feet and three hundred pounds. They leave the large bodies of water and go up the rivers to spawn. They, too, once were common.

Then large commercial fisheries came to the eastern seaboard, to the big rivers, to the Great Lakes. At first the sturgeon were not taken as commercially marketable fish. But because they were sluggish, they were caught in great numbers in the fishermen's nets, and because they were big, they tore the nets to pieces. So the fishermen made a practice of throwing them—thousands on thousands of them—onto the banks of rivers and lakes to rot in the sun or be used for pig feed or fertilizer.

Later came the realization that sturgeon meat is good to eat, and that American sturgeon could supply as good caviar as that imported from Europe. So then the sturgeon went into the fisheries—as long as they lasted.

They might have lasted a little longer, except for two things that happened as the United States became more thickly populated. Dams were built in some of the rivers, and so the fish could no longer reach their spawning beds. And the water of lakes, rivers, and estuaries became polluted, as chemical wastes from industrial plants and garbage and sewage from cities were dumped into them. So the big fish died from poisoning, or the small water animals—their food—were killed, and they had nothing to eat.

Today a few Atlantic sturgeon are still caught along the coast, but they weigh, at the most, three hundred or three hundred and fifty pounds; most of them are much smaller than that. A few lake sturgeon, two to three feet long, are caught, perhaps through the ice in winter fishing. No one knows how many of either kinds are left, but both are rare. Where thousands of pounds were once caught every year in a locality, today only one or two fish are taken, or none at all.

Some states now protect the sturgeon completely, or allow only one or two to be taken by each fisherman. In some lakes and rivers, campaigns to clean up pollution are helping them. Where dams stop their spawning runs, fish passages are being built to let them go around the dams. So perhaps eastern America may, after all, keep this remarkable fish that has survived from ancient times.

Western America, too, has its sturgeons. One, the white sturgeon, is credited with being North America's largest freshwater fish; an early-day catch of one weighing eighteen hundred pounds was recorded from the Fraser River in Canada. It was common in the big rivers of the Pacific Coast, where it probably, in early days, often weighed up to a thousand pounds. But here, too, the sturgeon were heavily fished commercially, and the supply quickly decreased. Today, again, no one knows how many white sturgeon there are.

However, they are protected by state laws—and in a very unusual way. On the Snake River in Idaho, for example, a white sturgeon can be too large to keep. If it is six feet long or more, the fisherman must throw it back! In this way, fish of spawning size are protected; and so they can produce, for many years, the eggs that will constantly renew the supply of young fish.

GREAT LAKES FISH AND
THE SEA LAMPREY

On the Great Lakes, in the late 1800s and early 1900s, a tremendous fishing industry thrived, taking fish for canning, for smoking, and for delivery fresh to markets. Sturgeon were an important part of the catch, and so, too, were several members of the salmon family, all of them having the delicious meat for which salmon and trout are famous.

There were the big lake trout, of which many millions of pounds a year were taken. There were whitefish and several kinds of cisco, so closely related that they themselves are sometimes called whitefish; they also are often called "chub." Among them, they seemed to furnish an endless supply of food that has always ranked with our finest.

But the supply didn't turn out to be endless. An unbelievable number of fish were caught each year, and for those that remained, man was changing their habitat. Pollution seeped through their water, destroying their food; obstructions clogged their streams.

Then into their streams and lakes came a deadly enemy.

In 1913 to 1918 the Welland Ship Canal between Lake Ontario and Lake Erie was made deeper; and in the years immediately afterward, the sea lampreys moved west. Originally they had come up the St. Lawrence River from the sea but had not traveled farther westward than Lake Ontario. But now they spread rapidly through Lake Erie, Lake Huron, Lake Michigan, and Lake Superior, and established themselves in great numbers. And they are a death-dealing enemy to trout, whitefish, and cisco.

The lamprey looks like an eel but is not one. It has a round suction mouth lined with teeth and centered with a file-like tongue. The suction mouth fastens itself to the side of a fish, and the teeth and tongue bore in; the lamprey sucks the fish dry of blood and other body liquids.

Ciscoes are a fine catch for winter fishing through the ice.

In only a few years the fish in the lakes had dropped to a small fraction of their former numbers. By then, man had started an all-out campaign against the lampreys, and succeeded in killing many thousands of them. But the lamprey is hard to deal with. It runs up small streams to spawn, and the newly hatched young bury themselves in a muddy stream bed and stay there for nine or ten years or longer. Only when they are mature do they leave the stream and drift back to the lake, to become the parasite that fastens on a fish and gorges itself.

So the campaign to get rid of them is double-barreled. It tries to trap the adults as they go upstream to spawn; it tries to poison the young in the small streams where they spend their early years.

The men who are doing the work are hopeful that they are at least getting the lamprey under control. There are fewer adults. There are more fish—at least, of some kinds.

There is still a commercial lake-trout catch—perhaps a half-million pounds from the three lakes that in the 1930s were producing fifteen million pounds a year. There are more whitefish than there were for years. There may be more of the cisco that is called "lake herring." All of these fish live in the Great Lakes and in other deep, clear, cold lakes of the northern states and Canada.

But three kinds of cisco, all once so abundant in Lake Michigan and Lake Huron that they were the most important "chub" of the big fisheries, may be gone forever. Two of them were the largest two of the ciscoes—the blackfin and the deep-water ciscoes. Neither kind has been seen in the two lakes for more than fifteen years. Of the third, the longjaw cisco, only seven were found in a recent two-year study. So it seems that control of the lamprey and protection against overfishing came too late to save these fine fish.

THE SALMON

It might seem that in trying to wipe out the lamprey from the Great Lakes, man is making his same old mistake—that of trying to protect one kind of animal by wiping out an animal that preys on it, and so disturbing the balance by which nature assures life to all kinds of living things. But there is a difference here.

True enough, man has disturbed the balance. But he did it when he changed the Great Lakes as a habitat—when he dug a canal that allowed this terrible enemy to enter lakes where the whitefish and trout and cisco lived. This is not a situation that had existed for thousands of years, with the fish surviving in spite of it. It is a condition that developed suddenly, in five to ten years; and the fish could not adjust to it.

A few Montana graylings still survive, although their close relative, the Michigan grayling, is gone forever.

So it is with many kinds of fish today, whose numbers are so reduced that they may be on the edge of extinction; and with others that are losing ground so fast that they, too, may become endangered. Man has suddenly changed their habitat, in one way or another, and they cannot adjust. So we lose them. And so man's foremost effort to save almost any kind of fish is to repair the damage he has done to their habitat.

We have several kinds of splendid salmon in the West—the chinook or king salmon, the silver or coho, the red or sockeye, and others. We know well the story of their leaving the ocean each year and swimming up the rivers in tremendous numbers, to spawn. But these hordes are being steadily reduced, by dams in the rivers, and by pollution of the water.

On the east coast we have another kind, the Atlantic salmon. This fine fish is common along the Atlantic shores of Europe, and once was common in our own New England, running up the big rivers each year to spawn. Today it is rare there, and in danger. A few are found in only eight rivers, all in Maine. The Atlantic salmon, too, is a victim of dams in streams and of pollution.

Best efforts to help the salmon are to repair some of the damage done to their habitat. Campaigns are under way to clean up pollution of the water and to improve passages for fish around the dams. These efforts will help other fish too—the sturgeon, and the shad, which is like the salmon in its spawning habits and is another fine fish that is becoming more and more rare.

THE GRAYLING

Various other kinds of fish have been greatly reduced by changes men have made in their habitat. One of these is the grayling, a troutlike fish that is a favorite catch of the fly-rod fisherman.

Once a Michigan subspecies of the grayling was unbelievably abundant in that state's cold forest streams. But the forests were cut, and the water in the unshaded streams became warmer. Soil washed down from unprotected watersheds and covered the gravelly bottoms with mud. And logs were sent shooting downstream, often destroying the grayling's eggs and young in the spawning beds. Along with all this, the grayling was heavily fished. So today in Michigan, once known as "The Grayling State," the grayling is extinct.

His western relatives may fare a little better. For the Montana grayling, too, the habitat was changed by lumbering; by mining, that dumped poisonous mine-tailings into the streams; by agriculture, in which water running off the fields contaminated the streams with DDT and other insecticides. The effect that these chemicals have on fish has been dramatically demonstrated in recent years by fish kills along some of the big rivers, in which millions of fish of many kinds were left dead along the banks.

But the Montana grayling still lives in a few high, clean mountain streams and lakes in Montana and other Rocky Mountain states, where they are protected from heavy fishing. And another subspecies, the Arctic grayling, is still abundant in the lakes and streams of Alaska and western Canada. So, armed with knowledge and a desire to protect them, man can hope that these two kinds of grayling will not follow the route of the Michigan grayling to extinction.

THE CUTTHROAT TROUT

Some kinds of trout are another challenge to man to protect the clear, cool streams and lakes that shelter them. Among those most affected are the cutthroat or "native" trout in many western localities—a trout that gets its name from a slash of bright red

Cutthroat trout, once abundant in the mountains of the West, are threatened with extinction as the mountain streams change.

color across its throat. When white men first came to the West, these were the trout they most often took. But, again, lumbering and mining changed the streams, and the cutthroat became more and more rare. Then fish and game departments of the various states, in order to give the fisherman his catch, imported trout of different kinds and restocked the streams. Among them were, for example, brown trout, easily raised in hatcheries but greedy feeders; and they were soon competing heavily for food with the remaining cutthroats.

Today a few of the cutthroats still live in western streams and lakes. There are various subspecies in different localities; most of them, if not all, may be in danger of extinction. Of some kinds, we know that there are only a few hundred; of others, the number existing is not known. Efforts to raise them in hatcheries have not been very successful; so we know that the best way to protect and increase them is improvement of their own natural habitat.

Will man be able to accomplish this improvement? Or will the cutthroats go the way of the Michigan grayling? The years will tell, for the cutthroats, and for some other trout too—the Sunapee trout in two ponds in Maine and New Hampshire, the Apache trout in Arizona, and others.

THE LONELY ONES

There are a good many other fish that we may lose from our lakes and streams. Quite a large number of kinds live only in one locality—only a few fish in a single isolated stream or pond or spring.

The Devil's Hole pupfish, for example, is a tiny, inch-long fish that lives only in a spring near Death Valley. The desert dace lives in warm springs in Nevada. The Big Bend gambusia lives in two pools in Big Bend National Park. The Ozark cavefish is seen only in a few caves in southwestern Missouri. The Maryland

darter has never been seen except in one small stream in Maryland. Most of these kinds of fish are quite small; giant among
them is the largest of our minnows, the five-foot Colorado River
squawfish that is still seen occasionally in the Colorado River.

Most rarities like these are under strict protection; their creek
or pond or spring is in a national park or other sanctuary where
catching them is strictly prohibited. So perhaps they will survive,
and remain there for us to see them—the lonely ones.

Chapter 11

CAN WE SAVE OUR ANIMALS?

The answer is *yes!* At least, we can save most of the endangered species, if all of us work at it. Two great nations are working together to save the whooping cranes, with the help of such powerful organizations as the National Audubon Society and interested individuals all along the migration route of the cranes, from northern Canada to southern Texas. State and national governments are working together to save the California condor, and they are also aided by organizations and individuals; and this is true of the Kirtland's warbler and some other threatened species.

The trumpeter swan and the beaver, forced to the very brink of extinction by man's greed, have been drawn back to safety by man's untiring efforts to save them. And remnants of the buffalo, once so numerous on our prairies and plains, have been saved.

But what of the alligator, one of our most interesting animals? In spite of laws to protect him and other efforts in his behalf, his numbers are rapidly diminishing. One thing can save him, and it will take all of us working together to bring it about. If all the people in America will stop buying articles of alligator skins— shoes and bags and billfolds and hatbands and other articles— there will be no market for alligator hides, and poachers will stop killing the alligators. It's as simple as that! The alligators will live

A young whooping crane drinking, with a watchful eye for danger.

in peace and reproduce their kind in the few wetlands that are left to them.

Widespread publicity—telling people what is happening to their valuable natural resources and interesting them in saving their treasures—is one of the most effective ways of preserving our wildlife. Take the case of the whooping cranes. Practically all the people in the United States and Canada are interested in saving this magnificent bird because they have been informed about him. Every fall, newspapers all over the country tell how many cranes arrive at their wintering grounds from their northern nesting sites. When an injured crane is found and saved or a baby crane is hatched in captivity or any other bit of news develops about the whoopers, everyone reads about it with great interest.

In the same way, people need to be informed about other wildlife that they are in danger of losing forever. They need to understand that the nation's great natural and recreational resources belong to them, to preserve and cherish. We often hear the slogan, "You can't stop progress," and no doubt this is true. But we need to know the meaning of progress. We need to know the difference between real progress and the schemes of special groups who are attempting to exploit national resources for their own gain. For example, would dams in the Grand Canyon be real progress—for the good of all—or would they be exploitation for a few? Is draining fresh water from the Florida Everglades—and the possible destruction of Everglades National Park—for the good of all, or, again, is it exploitation for a few?

WILDLIFE ORGANIZATIONS

So many national, state, and local governments, and so many organizations are working on the problems concerned with preserving our wildlife that the National Wildlife Federation's Conservation Directory takes ninety-five pages to tell about them.

Included are the National Audubon Society, the National Wildlife Federation, Defenders of Wildlife, the Wildlife Management Institute, Nature Conservancy, Wilderness Society, American Ornithologists' Union, Sierra Club, Isaac Walton League, World Wildlife Fund, and many others. Young people's organizations on the list are Boy Scouts, Girl Scouts, Campfire Girls, Brotherhood of the Jungle Cock, and Future Farmers of America.

Recognizing that the hope for future conservation and wise use of our national resources lies in young people, at least two leading adult conservation organizations work closely with them. These are the National Audubon Society and the National Wildlife Federation.

The National Audubon Society has enrolled more than thirteen million school children in its Audubon Junior Clubs since 1910, and furnished them with inexpensive natural-history material. The Society also maintains four Audubon centers in various parts of the country, in which children and their teachers can learn about nature first hand. And it has four summer camps for teachers and other adult youth leaders.

But this is just one phase of the work of the Audubon Society. It has done a tremendous job, not only in informing the American public of what is happening to our natural resources, but in actually preserving some of these resources. In addition to maintaining more than forty wildlife sanctuaries across the country, it has helped other organizations and government agencies to establish sanctuaries, wildlife refuges, and nature centers. It also constantly carries on intensive research on wildlife that provides valuable information on the habits and needs of threatened species. The National Society's bimonthly magazine, *Audubon*, goes to all its members. *The Curious Naturalist* is for younger readers.

There are more than three hundred affiliated state and local Audubon societies; these are important conservation leaders in their communities, and many of them help to establish and maintain wildlife sanctuaries.

The National Wildlife Federation has nearly seventy-five hundred affiliated organizations in forty-nine states, as well as several hundred thousand individual associate members. Its objectives, as stated on the masthead of its magazine, *National Wildlife*, are: "To create and encourage an awareness among the people of this nation of the need for wise use and proper management of those resources of the earth upon which the lives and welfare of men depend: the soil, the water, the forests, the minerals, the plant life, and the wildlife."

Like the Audubon Society, the Wildlife Federation is attempting to reach and inform the young people of our country. Each year it publishes and distributes more than three hundred thousand pieces of conservation literature to school children, teachers, and other youth leaders, in addition to the news releases which it furnishes to the press and to TV and radio stations.

For younger children the Wildlife Federation sponsors Ranger Rick's Nature Club and publishes *Ranger Rick's Nature Magazine*, which is sent to all club members. This magazine has such interesting stories about wildlife and such beautiful full-color pictures that children who receive it are likely to find their older brothers and sisters reading it too. Each member of Ranger Rick's Club pledges:

To train my mind to learn the importance of nature.

To use my hands to help protect our soil, water, woods and wildlife.

And, by my good example, to show others how to respect, properly use and enjoy our natural resources.

In addition to the fellowships awarded each year to graduate college students for research in conservation and natural-resource management, the National Wildlife Federation helps numerous other important research projects. It also sponsors, during the first week in spring, the annual National Wildlife Week. And it carries on a National and State Conservation Achievement Program, in which state and national awards are made annually to conservation leaders.

In conservation, and especially wildlife conservation, new developments occur and conditions change almost overnight. While this book was being written, ivory-billed woodpeckers were sighted in Texas; the Maui nukupuu was rediscovered in Hawaii; whooping cranes broke all records and had a 7,216-acre tract added to their refuge in Texas; new pressures developed, and new legislation was passed.

Wildlife conservation magazines, news bulletins, and pamphlets are doing a fine job of keeping readers up to date on important developments. In addition to the ones mentioned above, some of these are: *The Nature Conservancy News; Defenders of Wildlife News; National Geographic* magazine; *Natural History* magazine and *Nature and Science,* for children (American Museum of Natural History); *Outdoor News Bulletin* (Wildlife Management Institute).

GOVERNMENT AGENCIES

The Department of the Interior leads the numerous national government agencies charged with preserving our natural resources, because its main purpose is conservation. This Department has the National Parks, where no hunting is allowed; and the Bureau of Sport Fisheries and Wildlife, under the Fish and Wildlife Service, which is working hard to save threatened species.

The National Wildlife Refuges—more than three hundred of them, totaling over twenty-eight million acres—are under the administration of the Bureau of Sport Fisheries and Wildlife. They are found in all but five states and are known by the "Sign of the Flying Goose." They are mainly for migratory birds, but small mammals also live in most of them; and some are the home of big-game animals, such as moose, pronghorns, bison, and elk. Some of them, as we have seen, furnish protection for threatened species.

In October 1966, Congress passed the Endangered Species Preservation Act, which gave the Secretary of the Interior authority to set up a comprehensive program for the protection, conservation, and propagation of endangered species of fish and

Myriads of wild ducks take advantage of the protection offered by the Sacramento Migratory Waterfowl Refuge in California.

wildlife. An Office of Endangered Species, under the Bureau of Sport Fisheries and Wildlife, was established to find out which species are endangered and what can be done to save them.

Years before the passage of this Act, however, wildlife refuges and wildlife research laboratories and centers, such as the Patuxent Center, were working on these problems. Numerous other government agencies are doing research in the whole conservation area, and so are colleges and universities across the country; in fact, many of them are offering courses and giving degrees in land and wildlife management.

Curiously enough, while one branch of the Bureau of Sport Fisheries and Wildlife worked to preserve wildlife, another branch helped put some of the species on the endangered list. This was the Division of Predator and Rodent Control. When man unbalanced the balance of nature in his haste to clear the land and replace wildlife with his domestic animals, he was faced with getting rid of the predators who killed his livestock. He called on the national government for help, and the predator control division sent out men with traps and poison to eliminate the mountain lions, wolves and coyotes, and other predators.

Then, when there were no longer enough predators to keep the rodents under control, the ground squirrels and prairie dogs and gophers began to eat the crops. So they, too, had to be destroyed. Among the victims—now threatened with extinction—of this widespread trapping and poisoning program were mountain lions, red wolves, prairie dogs, black-footed ferrets, and others.

Today the policy for predator and rodent control is changing, and the division has a new name—the Division of Wildlife Services. Control of "pest" animals will be kept to the minimum "needed to protect other resources and human health." Extensive research is being carried on to find specific controls for pest species. And where possible, efforts are aimed at getting rid of only an individual "problem predator" instead of his whole tribe; that is, if a mountain lion in a certain locality turns to killing sheep and cattle, he should be eliminated. But no general campaign will thereupon be launched against mountain lions.

Perhaps we should point out here that the unhappy results of unbalancing the balance of nature are not confined to North America. They occur all over the world. In the summer of 1967, newspapers carried the story of an "army" of millions of field mice that swept across portions of Bosnia, in Yugoslavia, and completely wiped out the crops of an estimated five thousand farmers. The appearance of field mice in such enormous numbers was believed due to the fact that foxes, the natural enemies of field mice, have been largely killed off in Bosnia.

THE GREAT NEED FOR HABITAT

Probably the two greatest threats to wildlife are loss of habitat and the widespread use of pesticides, and they are both tough problems to solve. A wildlife species not only needs enough space for its habitat, it has to have the right habitat. We can't just shove it into some area that is too poor for our needs, and expect it to exist there—it just won't do it!

The Bureau of Sport Fisheries and Wildlife, assisted by aviculturists, is attempting to breed in captivity threatened bird species—whooping cranes, Laysan ducks, Nene geese, and others. But this does not solve the problem unless these birds can be restored to their wild state. As *Audubon* magazine so aptly puts it, "The biologist knows that a species has come to the end of the trail when we are down to a captive population."

Settlers should have heeded the *Tickler Magazine* way back in 1821 when it printed the following admonition—reprinted in *Audubon* magazine (July-August 1967)—"The fault is great in man or woman who steals a goose from off a common; but what can plead that man's excuse who steals a common from a goose?"

We've been stealing the "common" from the "goose" for a good many years, and now we're suffering the consequences.

It is not easy to restore wildlife habitat when so much of it is covered with cities and towns, with great industrial complexes, and with thousands of miles of concrete highways. On the other hand, we still have great wilderness areas and wetlands, which conservationists are working to preserve, and there are many smaller areas, such as woodlands and lake shores and river banks, that have not yet been overrun by land developments and industry.

Many cities and towns have parks and sanctuaries and nature centers, where wildlife is protected and people can see and enjoy it, and many farmers and ranchers are preserving the wildlife on their land. The famous King ranch in Texas is a good example of this. There is a great concentration of wildlife on this million-acre ranch, and scientific principles of conservation are practiced, including the employment of a full-time wildlife-management director. Some developers are beginning to realize how important wildlife is and are providing for it in their land operations. And some industrialists are doing what they can to help in the conservation movement by providing money for research and publicity.

POLLUTION

The widespread use of pesticides—sprays to kill insects and weeds—has become a danger, not only to wildlife, but to humans as well. These sprays are in the air and in the water; they contaminate sea food and, sometimes, pollute our drinking water. Industrial plants that belch forth smoke also pollute the air, and so do the exhausts from America's millions of automobiles. Cities and towns that deposit sewage and other wastes into rivers and lakes and bays are polluting the water.

Studies are being made to learn the extent of air and water pollution and to find ways and means of reducing or eliminating it.

Chemical companies are trying to find formulas for pesticides that will not be harmful to people and wildlife. Bills are constantly being introduced in Congress and in our state legislatures which are designed to check pollution and to preserve our natural resources, including wildlife. A bill to control air pollution was passed by Congress in 1967.

How can we help to save our animals in danger? There are many ways. For one thing, we can learn more about wildlife and the things that are threatening it. We can read the current wildlife magazines in our libraries and find out about conservation bills in Congress. Then we can write to our Congressmen to support these bills, and we can ask relatives and friends to write to the Congressmen.

A school nature club and a nature center in the community help to arouse interest in preserving wildlife. The National Audubon Society has a department for the express purpose of giving advice and guidance concerning nature centers. It is the Nature Centers Division, National Audubon Society, 1130 Fifth Avenue, New York, New York 10028.

Hunters can refrain from shooting at living things just for the fun of shooting. People who live in rural areas can learn about hawks and owls and other birds, and snakes and other reptiles, that are friends of the farmer, because they feed on rodents and insects that destroy crops. When clearing land, farmers can leave a patch of woods where wild things can take refuge, and some brush and tall grass along the fences and ditch banks where quail and other birds can hide and make their nests.

And, as they grow older, young people can continue to keep informed, so that when they become adults, they will be able to take an even more important part in helping to preserve our wildlife and other natural resources and in teaching others to preserve them.

BIBLIOGRAPHY

If a book is especially intended for younger readers, the age level is noted—for example: 10–12.

Adrian, Mary. *The American Alligator*. Hastings, 1967. 7–10.
——*The North American Bighorn Sheep*. Hastings, 1966. 7–10.
——*The North American Wolf*. Hastings, 1965. 7–9.
Allen, Durward L. *Our Wildlife Legacy*. Funk, 1962.
Allen, Robert Porter. *On the Trail of Vanishing Birds*. McGraw, 1957.
——*The Whooping Crane*. National Audubon Society, 1952.
Annixter, Jane and Paul. *The Great White*. Holiday, 1966. 12–16.
Arnov, Boris, Jr. *Secrets of Inland Waters*. Little, 1965. 11–14.
Audubon Nature Encyclopedia: Twelve volumes. Curtis, 1965. 10 up.
Banko, Winston E. *Trumpeter Swan*. U.S. Fish and Wildlife Service, 1960.
Barker, Will. *Familiar Animals of America*. Harper, 1956.
Beebe, B. F. *American Desert Animals*. McKay, 1966. 10 up.
——*American Lions and Cats*. McKay, 1963. 7–11.
——*Coyote, Come Home*. McKay, 1963. 10 up.
Birds in Our Lives. U.S. Fish and Wildlife Service, 1966.
Broley, Myrtle Jeanne. *Eagle Man*. Pellegrini, 1952.
Burger, Carl. *All About Cats*. Random, 1966. 10–12.
——*All About Fish*. Random, 1960. 10 up.
Burton, Maurice. *In Their Element* (whales, seals, sea otter, manatee, beaver). Abelard, 1960. 10 up.
Byrd, Ernestine N. *Ice King* (polar bear). Scribner's, 1965. 8–12.
Cahalane, Victor H. *Mammals of North America*. Macmillan, 1961.
Callison, Charles H., Editor. *America's Natural Resources*. Ronald, 1967.

Carr, Archie. *So Excellent a Fishe* (green turtle). Natural History Press, 1967.

Carson, Rachel. *Silent Spring*. Houghton, 1962.

Colby, C. B. *Wild Dogs* (wolves, coyote). Duell, 1965. 10 up.

——*Wild Rodents*. Meredith, 1967. 10 up.

Dufresne, Frank. *No Room for Bears*. Holt, 1965.

Easton, Robert, and Smith, Dick. *California Condor: Vanishing American*. McNally and Toftin: Lane Book Co., 1964. 12–14.

Eckert, Allan W. *The Silent Sky: The Incredible Extinction of the Passenger Pigeon*. Little, 1965.

Farb, Peter. *The Face of North America* (Young Reader's Edition). Harper, 1964. 12 up.

——*The Land and Wildlife of North America*. Time-Life, 1964.

Fenton, Carroll Lane, and Carswell, Evelyn. *Wild Folk in the Desert*. John Day, 1958. 10 up.

Gabrielson, Ira N. *Wildlife Conservation*. Macmillan, 1959.

Gray, Robert. *Children of the Ark* (rescue of the world's vanishing wildlife). Norton, 1968. 10–14.

Hutchins, Ross E. *The Last Trumpeters*. Rand, 1967. 7 up.

Hylander, Clarence J. *Animals in Armor*. Macmillan, 1954. 10 up.

——*Feathers and Flight*. Macmillan, 1951. 12–16.

——*Fishes and Their Ways*. Macmillan, 1964. 12–16.

——*Wildlife Communities*. Houghton, 1966. 12 up.

Koford, Carl B. *The California Condor*. National Audubon Society, 1953; Dover Publications, 1966.

Laycock, George. *Big Nick* (black bear). Norton, 1967. 10–14.

——*The Sign of the Flying Goose* (National Wildlife Refuges). Natural History Press, 1965.

McClung, Robert M. *Black Jack* (alligator). Morrow, 1967. 8–12.

——*The Mighty Bears*. Random, 1967. 8–12.

——*Screamer, Last of the Eastern Panthers*. Morrow, 1964. 8–11.

McCoy, J. J. *The Hunt for the Whooping Cranes*. Lothrop, 1966. 12 up.

McNulty, Faith. *The Whooping Crane*. Dutton, 1966.

Mannix, Dan. *The Last Eagle*. McGraw, 1966. 12 up.

Matthiessen, Peter. *Wildlife in America*. Viking, 1959.

Mayfield, Harold. *The Kirtland's Warbler*. Cranbrook Institute of Science, Bloomfield Hills, Michigan, 1960.

Miracle, Leonard. *That Cougar Is a Puma.* Putnam, 1966. 10 up.

Murphy, Robert, *The Peregrine Falcon.* Houghton, 1963.

Our Living World of Nature: Ten volumes. McGraw, 1966, 1967. 10 up.

Perry, John. *Our Polluted World.* Watts, 1967. 12 up.

Peterson, Roger Tory, and Fisher, James. *Wild America.* Houghton, 1955.

Pettingill, Olin Sewall, Jr., Editor. *The Bird Watcher's America* (Kirtland's warbler, trumpeter swan, others). McGraw, 1965.

Pinney, Roy. *Vanishing Wildlife.* Dodd, Mead, 1963.

Pruitt, William O., Jr., *Animals of the North.* Harper, 1967. 12 up.

Rare and Endangered Fish and Wildlife of the U.S. The U.S. Bureau of Sport Fisheries and Wildlife, 1966.

Redford, Polly. *Raccoons and Eagles.* Dutton, 1965.

Riedman, Sarah R., and Gustafson, Elton T. *Home is the Sea: for Whales.* Rand, 1966. 12 up.

Ripper, Charles L. *The Weasel Family.* Morrow, 1959. 8–12.

Seton, Ernest Thompson. *Biography of a Grizzly.* Schocken, 1967. (Various other editions of this classic since 1900.) 12 up.

Silverberg, Robert. *The Auk, the Dodo, and the Oryx.* Crowell, 1967. 12–16.

Stoutenburg, Adrien. *A Vanishing Thunder.* Natural History Press, 1967. 10–14.

Tanner, James T. *The Ivory-billed Woodpecker.* National Audubon Society, 1942; Dover Publications, 1966.

Teale, Edwin Way. *Autumn Across America.* Dodd, Mead, 1956.

——*Journey into Summer,* Dodd, Mead, 1960.

——*North with the Spring.* Dodd, Mead, 1951.

——*Wandering Through Winter.* Dodd, Mead, 1965.

Walden, Howard T. 2d. *Familiar Freshwater Fishes of America.* Harper, 1964.

Waterfowl Tomorrow. U.S. Bureau of Sport Fisheries and Wildlife, 1964.

Wild Animals of North America. National Geographic Society, 1960.

Wondrous World of Fishes. National Geographic Society, 1965.

Wood, Dorothy. *The Bear Family.* Harvey, 1966. 8 up.

——*The Cat Family.* Harvey, 1968. 8 up.

INDEX

Page numbers in *italics* indicate pages on which illustrations appear.

175

About the Authors

Frances and Dorothy Wood grew up on a ranch in western Colorado, where they knew firsthand the wildlife that became their first writing interest—and where they learned to ride and fish and enjoy the outdoors.

Frances Wood attended Colorado State College and the University of Colorado, and was a high-school teacher in Colorado schools. Dorothy Wood attended Colorado State University, Colorado College, and the University of Chicago. Both were for many years editors of elementary-school textbooks. All of their training and experience put a high premium on accuracy of observation and research, and made them familiar, as well, with the interests and needs of young readers.

Disturbed by what is happening to American wildlife, they determined to bring the story to America's young people. Two years, ten thousand miles, and hundreds of letters later, the manuscript was ready, drawn to a large extent from "on-the-spot" research—for example, at Aransas Wildlife Refuge, which the sisters visited while the whooping cranes were returning in the late fall of 1967.

Both authors have written many successful books for young readers. Frances Wood is the author of the six-volume series "Our National Parks" and several serials in *Children's Activities*, as well as many magazine articles. Dorothy Wood is the author of *Beavers; Plants with Seeds; Bear Family;* and *Cat Family*. They have each written several volumes in the "Enchantment of America" series.

The sisters now live in St. Petersburg, Florida.